The Little English Workbook

The Little English Workbook

Kathryn N. Benzel
University of Illinois
at Urbana–Champaign

Janne Goldbeck
Idaho State University

John Wiley and Sons, Inc.
New York • Chichester • Brisbane • Toronto

Preface

The objective of *The Little English Workbook* is to provide composition teachers with a set of self-contained exercises that are versatile enough to suit a variety of teacher and student needs. Several types of exercises are offered for each item discussed; each exercise is designed to provide students with concentrated drill on specific problems. Introductory material explains the basic rules of each section and serves to focus students' attention on particular problems to be corrected. The exercises themselves enable students both to recognize a particular pattern of usage and to generate that pattern. Wherever possible we also incorporate a process of revising and editing to develop students' ability to correct in context.

The *Workbook* maintains the same basic principles established in *The Little English Handbook*. We discuss those conventions of language that Edward P. J. Corbett has identified in the *Handbook* as necessary to correct the student writer's most common and persistent problems. We also adopt the *Handbook*'s terminology and the practice of stating general rules without the addition of subtle and often confusing exceptions. The organization of the *Workbook* corresponds closely to that of the *Handbook*, with sections on grammar, style, paragraphing, punctuation, and mechanics. For easy reference to the *Handbook*, we have numbered individual items in each major section as they are numbered in the *Handbook*. It should be noted, however, that although the *Workbook* has been developed to supplement the *Handbook*, the content and explanations are complete in themselves and can also be used separately or with other handbooks, in writing labs, by self-paced students, and in both remedial and regular composition classes.

We are indebted to Edward P. J. Corbett for his thorough review of the exercises and his helpful suggestions for their revision. We also thank Thomas O. Gay and Clifford Mills at Wiley for their careful attention in helping us to pre-

Preface

pare the manuscript. The project would not have been initiated, however, without the support and encouragement of the Center for Instructional Development at Idaho State University and former Director, Bari Lynn Gilliard, to whom we extend our special thanks.

Kathryn N. Benzel
Janne Goldbeck

Contents

Contents

Contents

Contents

Contents

Contents

Contents

Grammar

Use of Apostrophe for Possessives and Contractions
Items 20 and 21

Improper use of the apostrophe presents problems to readers. If an apostrophe is used incorrectly, it can change the writer's meaning. For example,

Bill and Julie's parents bought them a car. (The meaning is that Bill and Julie are brother and sister and that their parents bought them one car.)

Bill's and Julie's parents bought them a car. (Here the meaning is that there are two unrelated people, two sets of parents, and two cars.)

You can see that a misplaced or omitted apostrophe can change the reading of a sentence. Another problem for readers occurs when **its** (the possessive form of the pronoun **it**) and **it's** (the contraction of **it is**) are misused. For example, the two words are misused in the following sentences:

It's collar was lost. (should be **its**, that is, the dog's collar)

Its a collar that was lost. (should be **it's** here, the contraction **it is**)

Note the following rules for forming possessives and contractions.

1

Use of apostrophe for the possessive case of a noun

A. Most common English nouns form the possessive case by adding **'s** (singular) or **s'** (plural). Study the following sentences and note the possessive forms.

1

Use of Apostrophe for Possessives and Contractions

The **boy's** ball rolled into the street. (sing.)
The three **boys'** mothers called them to dinner. (pl.)

The squirrel ran away with the **dog's** bone. (sing.)
The **dogs'** leashes were left behind. (pl.)

The **teacher's** desk was cluttered. (sing.)
The **teachers'** meeting lasted two hours. (pl.)

B.   The plural forms of some English nouns are **not** formed by adding **s**. These nouns form their plural possessive by adding **'s**.

The **man's** coat was stolen. (sing.)
The **men's** softball game was postponed. (pl.)

The **child's** toy was hidden. (sing.)
The **children's** bikes were locked. (pl.)

The **deer's** fawn rested in the shade. (sing.)
The **deer's** forage area was destroyed. (pl.)

C.   Nouns ending in **s** can be made possessive two ways, either of which is correct: The usual way of adding **'s** (Francis's car, the boss's order), or by simply adding **'** (Francis' car, the boss' order).

Franci**s's** car was destroyed in the wreck.
Francis' car was destroyed in the wreck.

The boss**'s** order was carried out fully.
The **boss'** order was carried out fully.

Apostrophe—Exercise **1**

Possessives

NAME _____

Change the first words to show singular or plural possession, as indicated in parentheses. If you are uncertain about a plural form, use a dictionary.

EXAMPLE: man (pl.) The **men's** club held its annual meeting.
            cat (sing.) The dog ate the **cat's** food.

1. moth (sing.) The _____ wings fluttered incessantly.

2. month (pl.) He asked for six _____ pay in advance.

3. citizen (pl.) The _____ votes were not counted.

4. team (sing.) His _____ clubhouse has been rebuilt.

5. mouse (pl.) The _____ holes were discovered by the crafty cat.

6. ox (pl.) The _____ yoke was left in the field.

7. Bess (sing.) _____ dress was torn by branches as she ran through the brush.

8. girl (pl.) The _____ soccer team was out of training.

9. man (pl.) The _____ annual golf tournament was rained out.

10. woman (pl.) The new bill was voted down by the _____ action group against sex discrimination.

Use of Apostrophe for Possessives and Contractions

2

Groups of nouns can show individual or joint possession. Pairs of nouns can show individual or joint possession. For example,

John and Mary's mother was a teacher. (one mother, jointly possessed)
John's and **Mary's** mothers are teachers. (two mothers, individually possessed)

The **men and women's** rugby team was controversial. (a rugby team on which both men and women perform)
The **men's** and **women's** locker rooms were clean. (two locker rooms, one for men and one for women)

Group nouns and compound nouns are made possessive by adding 's. Their plural possessive is formed by adding s to the first word and 's to the end of the unit. For example,

The **editor in chief's** decision was final. (sing.)
The **editors in chief's** comments were helpful. (pl.)
The **son-in-law's** car was brand new. (sing.)
The **sons-in-law's** duties were unclear. (pl.)

Apostrophe—Exercise 2

Joint possession

NAME _____

Change the first words to show individual or joint possession, or singular or plural possession, as indicated in parentheses. If you are uncertain about plural forms, use a dictionary.

EXAMPLE: Fred, Lisa (ind.) **Fred's** and **Lisa's** parents were absent.

1. Joe, Jim (joint) _____ mother was ill.

2. Karen, Melissa (ind.) _____ birthdays were on the same day.

3. men, women (ind.) The _____ Olympic trials were postponed.

4. mother-in-law (sing.) The _____ expectations were not easy for the new bride to live up to.

5. Commander in chief (pl.) The _____ final meeting created distrust among them.

6. summer, winter (ind.) The _____ clientele varied greatly at the beach resort.

7. Secretary of State (pl.) The _____ decision was not agreeable to the rulers of the countries.

8. Billy, Francis (joint) The church group met at _____ summer house.

9. passer-by (sing.) The dog nipped at the _____ pant leg.

10. Beth, Maria (ind.) The grand prize was awarded to both _____ apple pies.

Use of Apostrophe for Possessives and Contractions

Apostrophe—Exercise 3

Possession

NAME _____

Change the first word, as indicated in parentheses, to show singular, plural, or joint possession.

EXAMPLE: actor (sing.) The **actor's** line was not heard.
man (pl.) The **men's** club held its annual meeting.

1. Paul (sing.) _____ ball rolled into the street.

2. Fred, George (joint) _____ car placed first in the rally.

3. lady-in-waiting (pl.) The _____ flowers were not ready in time for the rehearsal.

4. it (sing.) His rusty, old wagon lay on _____ side.

5. hawk (pl.) They found no eggs in the _____ nests.

6. Keats (sing.) _____ odes have become known as examples of Romantic poetry.

7. woman (pl.) _____ clothes are constantly changing.

8. ox (sing.) The _____ yoke broke in the middle of plowing.

9. mother-in-law (pl.) The _____ were kind to the new brides.

10. Margaret, Bill (ind.) _____ books were left behind.

3

its and *it's*

Mistakes in the use of the apostrophe with the pronoun **it** result from the two **s** forms of the word **it**. **Its** is the possessive case of the pronoun **it**; **it's** is the contraction of **it is** or **it has**. Avoid the mistake of confusing **it's** with the possessive form of **it**, **its**. Note the following examples.

The dog broke **its** leg. (the leg of the dog)
It's a hot, humid day. (It is a hot, humid day.)

4

Contractions combine two words into one.

The apostrophe indicates that one or more letters have been omitted. Often contractions are confused with possessives, such as **its** with **it's** and **their** with **they're**. **Its** and **their** are possessive words without apostrophes and are used only as possessives. Study the following contractions:

I am	I'm
you are	you're
(he, she, it, who) is	he's, she's, it's, who's
(we, they) are	we're, they're

For **will**, use **'ll**
I will	I'll
you will	you'll
they will	they'll

for **would**, use **'d**
I would	I'd
you would	you'd
they would	they'd

The negatives of **are**, **is**, **could**, **do**, **does**, **should**, and **would** are formed by adding the contraction **n't**: **aren't**, **isn't**, **couldn't**, **don't**, **doesn't**, **shouldn't**, **couldn't**. Two exceptions are **will not** (won't) and **cannot** (can't). The negative contraction of **I am** is **I'm not**.

Agreement of Subject and Verb

Apostrophe—Exercise **4**

Contractions

NAME _____

Fill in the blanks to complete the following pattern showing contractions.

		CONTRACTION	NEGATIVE CONTRACTION
EXAMPLE:	we will	we'll	we won't
1.	_____	she'll	she won't
2.	it is	_____	it isn't
3.	_____	who's	who isn't
4.	I am	I'm	_____
5.	they are	_____	_____
6.	_____	they'd	they won't
7.	_____	_____	it won't
8.	you are	you're	_____
9.	he will	_____	_____
10.	_____	I'd	_____
11.	_____	_____	he isn't
12.	you will	_____	_____

Grammar

Agreement of Subject and Verb

Item 22

1

A verb agrees with its subject in person and number.

To write correctly, you must make verbs **agree** with their subjects. Study the faults in the following sentences and note how they have been corrected. The subjects are underlined once; the verbs, twice.

INCORRECT: He run the fastest mile in Ohio.
CORRECT: He runs the fastest mile in Ohio.

INCORRECT: They runs a fast two-mile relay.
CORRECT: They run a fast two-mile relay.

In the above sentences notice the difference between the singular form of the verb **run** (runs) and the plural form (run). Most verbs ending in a single **s** (**looks, dresses, flies**) are singular. Most verbs not ending in **s** are plural. Note the following list of examples:

SINGULAR	PLURAL
he looks	they look
he goes	they go
he seems	they seem
he makes	they make
he tries	they try
he plays	they play

Agreement of Subject and Verb

Agreement of Subject and Verb—Exercise 1

Select the Correct Verb

NAME _____

Decide which verb in parentheses agrees with the subject given and underline it.

1. students (ask, asks)

2. movies (appeal, appeals)

3. men (is, are)

4. plane (fly, flies)

5. Doris (eat, eats)

6. water (drip, drips)

7. chefs (cook, cooks)

8. grandmother (knit, knits)

9. players (shoot, shoots)

10. secretaries (type, types)

2

There are some special situations involving the agreement of subject and verb.

A. Compound subjects
1. Singular subjects joined by **and** take a plural verb.

Susan and her brother run six miles every day.

2. Singular subjects joined by **or** or by correlative conjunctions (**either ... or, neither ... nor**) take a singular verb.

Susan or her brother runs six miles every day.
Neither Susan nor her brother runs six miles every day.

3. When both subjects are plural, the verb is plural.

The brothers and sisters run six miles every day.

4. When one subject is singular and the other is plural, and the subjects are joined by **or** or by correlative conjunctions (either ... or, neither ... nor), the verb agrees in number with the closest subject.

Neither the brothers nor the sister appears to have run six miles.

B. Collective nouns as subjects
1. If the collective noun is considered as a group, the verb is singular.

The symphony orchestra plays its final performance tonight.
The number of recruits has increased.

2. If the collective noun is considered as individuals of a group, the verb is plural.

The welcoming committee want to extend their greetings.
The number of recruits have petitioned for new living quarters.

C. Expletive structures: **there is/are, there was/were**
1. If the delayed or real subject following the expletive **there** is singular, the verb is singular; if the subject is plural, the verb is plural.

There is an odor of onions in the kitchen.
There are several solutions to the problem.

Agreement of Subject and Verb

Agreement of Subject and Verb—Exercise 2

Subject Identification

NAME _____

Identify the subject of each sentence by underlining it. Is the verb singular or plural?

EXAMPLE: **singular**   The following <u>reason</u> is absurd.

_____ 1. The price of sugar is ridiculous.

_____ 2. The reasons for the quarrel are still unknown.

_____ 3. The dog and cat are running around the fence.

_____ 4. There are eighty tests on the desk.

_____ 5. The orchestra members are tuning their instruments.

_____ 6. Neither John nor Peter fails to yield the right of way.

_____ 7. The best of the apple trees has many blossoms.

_____ 8. Either the boss or his secretaries run the Xerox machine.

_____ 9. The reports of misdemeanors haven't arrived.

_____ 10. Yoga is a discipline that many try in order to soothe their nerves.

Agreement of Subject and Verb—Exercise **3**

Verb Selection

NAME _____

Write the correct present-tense form of the verb in parentheses.

1. Pen and pencils (be) _____ handy items.

2. The news of the car crash (stun) _____ the viewers.

3. Neither the players nor the coach (be) _____ happy.

4. Eight of the singers (have) _____ laryngitis.

5. The turtles and cat (get) _____ along quite well.

6. The new four-hundred dollar bills (scare) _____ the bank manager.

7. The poetry of William Carlos Williams (hint) _____ of the Imagist movement.

8. Either John or his brothers (need) _____ money for school.

9. The description of the tornadoes (scare) _____ me.

10. There (be) _____ three new band members.

Agreement of Subject and Verb

3

Special structures

A. The following indefinite pronouns are singular: **each, either, neither, one, everyone, everybody, no one, nobody, anyone, anybody, someone, somebody.**

One of the apples is ripe.
Each is present.

B. The following common words are plural: **several, few, both, many, some, any, none.** When the words **some, any, none,** and **all** are followed by a phrase, that phrase often helps you decide whether the words are singular or plural. Note the following examples:

Some of the pencils are dull. (plural)
Some of the food was frozen. (singular)

All of the tires were new. (plural)
All of the gasoline was spilled. (singular)

Note: Here **food** and **gasoline** in the prepositional phrases indicate a **mass** of something, and therefore, the **some** and **all** are to be construed as singular. **Pencils** and **tires** are **countable** items, and therefore, the **some** or **all** is to be construed as plural.

Agreement of Subject and Verb—Exercise **4**

Subject-verb Agreement

NAME _____

In the following sentences underline the subject once and the correct verb in parentheses twice.

1. (Is, Are) every one of these balls yours?

2. Neither of the students (were, was) afraid to work.

3. A few of the girls in my class (were, was) on the honor roll.

4. Everybody in the South (knows, know) what the Civil War was like.

5. Both of your brothers (is, are) in the Army.

6. Every one of our berry bushes (was, were) uprooted by the storm.

7. Several of the debate team members (seems, seem) nervous.

8. Each of the apple trees (needs, need) pruning.

9. One of your conclusions (is, are) easily refuted.

10. Not one of these students (has, have) finished the required homework.

Agreement of Subject and Verb

4

BE Verb

The **BE** verb has more distinct forms than the other verbs in the English language. To be sure that you correctly use this verb, study the following examples:

PRESENT TENSE

	SINGULAR	PLURAL
1st person	I am	we are
2nd person	you are	you are
3rd person	he, she, it is	they are

SIMPLE PAST TENSE

	SINGULAR	PLURAL
1st person	I was	we were
2nd person	you were	you were
3rd person	he, she, it was	they were

SIMPLE FUTURE TENSE

_____ will be

PAST PARTICIPLE
been

Agreement of Subject and Verb—Exercise **5**

Verb Selection

NAME _____

Some of the following sentences use the _BE_ verb properly; mark a _C_ in the blank in those sentences. If the verb is incorrect, make the necessary change in the blank.

1. She and her relatives are _____ hideous people, always trying to outdo each other.

2. That committee's decision are _____ forthright and far-reaching.

3. Clara, Dave's sister, is _____ afraid of riding roller coasters.

4. Bus depots be _____ dangerous, so police watch them carefully.

5. Great Britain were _____ America's greatest source for importing tobacco.

6. Bill went to Europe and be _____ ecstatic about the Louvre.

7. Once Mabel is removed from the hospital, she am _____ content.

8. The young pups were _____ hungry because their master hadn't returned to feed them.

9. Every Monday I are _____ happy because I can go to work.

10. Doing exercises every day are _____ healthful.

Agreement of Subject and Verb

Agreement of Subject and Verb—Exercise **6**

Subject-verb agreement

NAME _____

In each of the following sentences you must make a choice of verbs. Write the subject of each verb and then the correct verb form. Remember that the verb should agree in person and number with its subject.

EXAMPLE: The rose bush with thorns (was, were) beautiful.
<u>rose bush</u> <u>was</u>

1. Both of the runners on our relay team (look, looks) good.

2. Fourteen of the twenty students (are failing, is failing) the final exam.

3. The bus for the football team (leave, leaves) at 9:00 A.M.

4. This best-selling novel for adults (make, makes) good reading.

5. The musicians in the orchestra (was, were) the most artistic.

6. The pine tree with wide-spreading branches (was brushing, were brushing) the roof.

7. The secretaries in the office (work, works) long hours.

8. Some guards from the pool (were trying, was trying) to calm the mothers.

9. The ships along the waterfront (seem, seems) to be anchored.

10. The sound of the storm (was, were) strange and frightening.

Agreement of Subject and Verb—Exercise **7**

Subject-verb agreement

NAME _____

Using all of the rules for subject-verb agreement, correct the following sentences if necessary. If the sentence is correct, mark a C next to it. If there is an error, circle the mistake and correct it.

1. Every one of us have made it on the tennis team.

2. We all go swimming in Betty and Dennis's pool.

3. Everyone wants to do something if it's *in*.

4. Do you think Joyce want those old chairs in the basement?

5. One of the secretaries' excuses for being tardy are really farfetched.

6. Either the mice or the cat find the way out.

7. Many of the pies has been burned.

8. Some of the pasta in this spaghetti are not done.

9. Please give Denise her snack when she come home.

10. Until I confront an issue I don't realize the problems involved.

11. She been still dressing when I arrived.

12. Building log cabins were hard work for the young couple.

13. Martha and her sisters feels like they've been to Alaska and back.

14. The piano tuner, who lives in Spokane, only tunes pianos on weekends.

15. The mountain bluebird of the Rockies display a spectacular color.

16. Do you think Grandma like the apron I made her?

17. Learning about writing sometimes seem like a boring, hopeless task.

18. Are one of those boxes small enough?

Agreement of Subject and Verb

19. Each of the races is sure to be close.

20. If you loses your money in Las Vegas, don't come to see me.

21. The wildflowers of the Northwest is beautiful.

22. In order to sublet the apartment, the renters were to give the manager notice.

23. The teacher and the new student argues continually about transfer credits.

24. A new suit of clothes cost about $150.

25. The manager of the night clubs say he will not have live entertainment.

Agreement of Subject and Verb—Exercise 8

Proofreading for subject-verb agreement

NAME _____

Edit the following essay for subject-verb agreement.

TELEVISION: MODERN MAN'S DILEMMA

With all the devices for entertainment, people of the twentieth century has become passive. Television, the primary form of today's entertainment, does not provide man with the excitement to challenge or motivate. Actually TV only point out the absurdities of modern living—disaster in the news and in melodrama; that's a poor motivation for challenge.

But why exactly does modern man become so attached to TVs? The answer is simple, if people will admit it. People looks passively at the world; someone or something else have to be active. The way in which man watches TV is the way he view the world around him. Why go play football with the neighborhood kids when TV show the "pros" at work? Why try to stop crime in neighborhoods when Starsky and Hutch can do it?

Unfortunately this passive attitude of today's people have affected not only their involvement in the world but also their self-images. "Someone else can take care of it" is their response. But, by continually saying this, man is put in a position that do not allow him to reveal his expertise or to feel satisfaction from reward. If someone else always do it, how can an individual gains a sense of self-worth? And worse yet, once this state of inactivity occur man usually sits back even farther in his easy chair.

Grammar

Pronouns
Items 23 and 24

1

A pronoun must agree in number, person, and gender with its antecedent. A pronoun is a word that replaces a noun to avoid repetition. The antecedent is a word (the noun) to which a pronoun refers.

A.   If a noun is singular, the pronoun must be singular. If a noun is plural, the pronoun must be plural. Note the faults in the following examples and how they've been corrected.

INCORRECT: The **secretaries** got **her** wages.
CORRECT: The **secretaries** got **their** wages. (plural)

INCORRECT: The new-found **religion** did not reveal **their** truths to just anyone.
CORRECT: The new-found **religion** did not reveal **its** truths to just anyone. (singular)

B.   Also a pronoun must agree in person with its antecedent. If a noun is first, second, or third person, the pronoun must reflect that person. Study the following examples:

	SINGULAR	PLURAL
1st person	I	we
2nd person	you	you
3rd person	he, she, it	they

INCORRECT: My mother said **he** should mind **my** own business.
CORRECT: My mother said **I** should mind **my** own business.

Pronoun-Antecedent Agreement

INCORRECT: **Our family** does own that land. **You** have owned it for fifty years.

CORRECT: **Our family** does own that land. **We** have owned it for fifty years. (first person, plural)

C.   A pronoun must agree with its antecedent in gender. If a noun is feminine, masculine, or neuter, the pronoun must reflect that gender. Note the following example:

INCORRECT: The **billing** was not in **his** proper form.

CORRECT: The **billing** was not in **its** proper form.

Pronouns

Pronouns—Exercise 1

Choosing the Correct Pronoun

NAME _____

Underline the pronoun form in parentheses that would be preferred and indicate the pronoun's person and number.

EXAMPLE: One must keep (<u>himself</u>, themselves) fit with a healthy diet.
<u>3rd person, singular</u>

1. A person has to run (his, their) own life. _ _ _ _ _ _ _ _

2. The baby was found by (its, his) mother. _ _ _ _ _ _ _ _

3. Captain Kangaroo asked Mr. Greenjeans if (they, he) found the rabbit.

   _ _ _ _ _ _ _

4. After Michigan won the title (they, it) went to play in the Rose Bowl.

   _ _ _ _ _ _ _

5. Neither of them will give (their, his) sanction to the project.

   _ _ _ _ _ _ _

6. Each of the boys ran as fast as (he, they) could. _ _ _ _ _ _ _ _

7. Everyone must watch (his, their) own hot dog. _ _ _ _ _ _ _ _

8. One must work at least twenty years before (he, they) can be eligible for

   a pension. _ _ _ _ _ _ _ _

9. The committee (has, have) always voted according to (their, its) wives'

   say-so. _ _ _ _ _ _ _ _

10. Each girl must make certain (they, she) is on time. _ _ _ _ _ _ _ _

24

Pronouns—Exercise 2

Pronoun Selection

NAME _____

Substitute pronouns for the repeated nouns in the second sentence. The pronouns should reflect the proper number, person, and gender of their antecedents.

EXAMPLE: My sister asked Ron not to bring the dog.
                        She   it
                   ~~My sister~~ said that ~~the dog~~ would disrupt the party.

1. Dave gave Dora a new dress for a Christmas present.

    Dave thought Dora would like a new dress.

2. The governor's son went to a used-car dealer and bought a motorcycle.

    The motorcycle didn't cost the governor's son too much, but the motor-

    cycle makes a lot of noise.

3. The new rock band visited Detroit, Cincinnati, and Chicago.

    The wives of the band members also stopped with their husbands.

4. The high school seniors took about three hours to finish the test.

    The seniors needed about one hour longer to finish the test.

5. All the players on the basketball team have suffered injured knees this year.

    It makes one wonder why the players keep on playing.

6. Last night there was a TV special about a whale.

    The TV special showed people how the whale breathes.

7. Those children down the street are always picking on my dog.

    Last week the dog really got even with those children.

Pronouns

8. Everybody knows about those sales because the weekly flyer had a special advertisement.

However, the sales were not what the flyer said they would be.

9. My baby brother spilled orange juice all over Mother's new rug.

When Mother returned home, she was furious with baby brother.

10. While strolling through the woods, Fred spotted a mother bear and her cubs.

Fred was not frightened when the mother bear charged.

2

There are some troublesome pronoun structures which need careful attention. Make certain that the antecedent is clear to the reader or else you may end up confusing your reader.

A.   When two or more antecedents are joined by **and**, the pronoun is plural. Note the following examples:

Janice and I went to the dress shop, and then **we** had a soda.
If **Nancy and John** are lucky, **they** will beat **their** previous records.

B.   When the antecedent is a collective noun, the pronoun may be singular or plural depending on whether the noun is considered as a unit or individuals acting on their own. Note examples:

The **team** was not playing **its** best. (singular)
The **team** voted for **their** new captains. (plural)

C.   **Everyone, everybody, anybody, anyone**, and **each** take singular verbs and should be referred to by a singular pronoun.

INCORRECT: **Everyone** needs **their** toothbrush.
CORRECT: **Everyone** needs **his** toothbrush.

D.   **All**, **some**, and **none** are singular or plural depending on the context. The prepositional phrase following the noun specifies whether it is singular or plural. Note the example:

Some of the fabric lost **its** coloring. (singular)
Some of the young men turned in **their** draft cards. (plural)

E.   **This** and **that** are demonstrative pronouns which refer to a whole idea in a previous sentence rather than to a person or inanimate object. However, you must be cautious when using **this** or **that**. The best rule of thumb is to use **this** and **that** as a demonstrative adjective followed by a noun. See the following examples:

ACCEPTABLE: I enjoyed the mountains, but **this** revealed to me that I really prefer a vacation at the beach.
BETTER: I enjoyed the mountains, but **this experience** revealed to me that I really prefer a vacation at the beach.

Pronouns

Pronouns—Exercise 3

Choosing the Correct Pronoun

NAME _____

Choose the correct pronoun in parentheses and underline it.

EXAMPLE: Jane wanted to find out if the students passed (his, <u>their</u>) tests.

1. Don't you think sales clerks should be more courteous to (their, its) customers?

2. Studying grammar may help students improve (them, their) writing.

3. Try to ignore Pat and Tom; (they, them) are just trying to gain attention.

4. Doing daily exercises is not fun for lots of people; (she, they) would rather drink coffee.

5. The tennis team won their matches and (those, those victories) made (their, them) happy.

6. Anybody who wants to come along should get (their, his) jacket.

7. Some of the paint dried up in (its, their) can.

8. The family went to the church of (its, their) choice.

9. I would like to have a million dollars, but (that, that wealth) would make me frivolous.

10. Each of the new students should have (their, his or her) enrollment card.

Pronouns—Exercise **4**

Pronoun Selection

NAME _____

Write the correct pronoun in the blank and underline its antecedent.

EXAMPLE: <u>Mary</u> passed the biology test because <u>she</u> studied.

1. George and Lisa are planning a trip to British Columbia as soon as

   _____ save enough money.

2. Four students were running the university bookstore when the president

   dismissed _____ for incompetence.

3. Joe has a class schedule that interferes with _____ work schedule.

4. Don't you think all of the students need _____ own utensils?

5. The newspaper was discredited for abuse of the incumbent candidate,

   but _____ redeemed _____ by a public apology.

6. The President seems to feel that _____ proposal will be accepted
   by the senators.

7. Whenever Father arrives late, Mother really gives _____ a piece of

   _____ mind.

8. The City Council voted for _____ City Manager.

9. What if no one reads the advertisement? Then _____ won't shop at
   the new boutique.

10. Everyone said to Linda that _____ was a ravishing beauty.

Pronouns

Pronouns—Exercise 5

Correct Antecedent Agreement

NAME _____

In the following sentences indicate the number and person of the antecedent, and select the proper pronoun.

EXAMPLE: Doug and Karen were hoping that <u>they</u> could meet the train on time. (3rd person, plural)

1. The young boy and his dog started on _____ trip around the world.

2. The price of potatoes is not what _____ used to be.

3. The choir could not perform _____ Sunday best because of too many illnesses.

4. If the town sheriff is re-elected, _____ says _____ will stop dogs from barking.

5. My mother says that _____ cannot buy that new formal that I want.

6. The palm-reader said, "_____ should watch your wrist lines carefully. _____ will tell _____ future."

7. Harriet could not find _____ new brooch.

8. The master marksman could hit any target with _____ special pistol.

9. All of the babies were waiting to see _____ doctors.

10. Everyone needs to find _____ niche in the world.

11. Anyone who is not in bed in ten minutes will not get _____ dessert tomorrow.

12. You must find _____ jacket before boarding the train.

13. The booster club met for _____ weekly pep session.

14. Mark and I will come directly after _____ finish cleaning the car.

15. The maps do not indicate that city. How will Bob and Terry find

_____ way?

16. How is the mistress of ceremonies going to introduce _____ husband?

17. In South America, the people do a lot of handiwork so _____ can

sell _____ to tourists.

18. Each of the dominoes should be placed with _____ dotted side facing up.

19. The camera that Bertha bought is not the one _____ wanted.

20. The circus drove into town with all _____ animals leashed behind

_____ biggest van.

Grammar

Dangling Verbals
Item 25

An introductory verbal or verbal phrase must have its "doer" in the subject of the main clause. If the verbal is not attached to the proper agent, it is a **dangling** verbal. You should make certain that the subject of the main clause is the "doer" of the action specified in the preceding verbal phrase. Note the faults in the following examples and the way they have been corrected.

	VERBAL PHRASE	SUBJECT

INCORRECT: **Running through the woods, George's shoes** were lost.

	VERBAL PHRASE	SUBJECT

CORRECT: **Running through the woods, George** lost his shoes.

	VERBAL PHRASE	SUBJECT

INCORRECT: **To accomplish this end, it** is necessary for us to study grammar and usage.

	VERBAL PHRASE	SUBJECT

CORRECT: **To accomplish this end, we** must study grammar and usage.

Dangling Verbals—Exercise 1

Introductory Verbal Phrases

NAME _____

Correct the following sentences, which have dangling verbals, by rearranging the main clause in such a way that the subject of the clause will be the "doer" of the action indicated in the introductory verbal phrase.

EXAMPLE: To take off, the plane's engine was started by John.
To take off, John started the plane's engine.

1. Shining brightly, Francis watched the moon.

2. To finish the race, it was necessary for Juan to run faster than ever.

3. By rowing to the island, the mail could be picked up by Mary and Jack.

4. Walking to the top of the stairs, the alarm was tripped by Bill.

5. To bake the cake, butter and eggs were needed by Kay.

6. In developing the film, certain chemicals were necessary by the printer.

7. In memory of the veterans, the tree was planted by the club.

8. Injuring himself on the tire iron, the car was not tuned properly by the mechanic.

9. Weeding the five-mile radius, the garden was cleared by the prisoners.

10. Following her brother, the way home was discovered by Marian.

Dangling Verbals

Dangling Verbals—Exercise 2

Introductory Verbal Phrases

NAME _____

Some of the following sentences use verbal phrases correctly; place a C next to them. Correct those sentences that have dangling verbals by re-arranging the main clause in such a way that the subject of the clause will be the "doer" of the action indicated in the introductory phrase.

1. Falling head over heels in love, the marriage was arranged by Tom and Ann.

2. In looking for new shoes, Mary discovered how high prices were.

3. To accommodate the convention, extra rooms were reserved by the hotel manager.

4. Chopping the fire wood, it was necessary for Tim to split logs.

5. In training for the marathon, ten miles were run each day by Bill.

6. In eating strawberries and shortcake, the juice ran over Ted's new shirt.

7. Discovering the new trail, the mountain became a new interest for the local residents.

8. To start the mower, the handle was depressed by the young children.

9. To correct an error in judgment, the new road plan was proposed by the race judges.

10. In order to pick up a friend at the airport, Jim had to meet a 5:00 A.M. plane.

Combining Verbal Phrases and Main Clauses

Dangling Verbals—Exercise 3

Combining Verbal Phrases and Main Clauses

NAME _____

Complete the following sentences by combining the verbal phrases and the main clauses. It may be necessary to reword the main clauses so as to identify clearly the "doer" of the verbal phrase's action.

1. it was necessary for Dennis to view the line-up
   to identify the criminal

2. the police received a call from the kidnappers
   threatening the hostage's life

3. the bear frightened the girl scouts
   shouting for help

4. the gospel was sung by the choir
   envisioning the splendor of heaven

5. the opportunity to embezzle funds was taken by Mr. Jones
   while managing the Hotel Lorraine

6. the pills were miscounted by the pharmacist
   while filling the prescription

7. the local address had to be maintained by Ron for six months
   to establish residency

8. the police officer was not relieved on time
   forgotten by the new recruit

9. the whistle was blown by the engineer
   before arriving at the train station

10. John heard the autumn wind
    blowing through the pine trees

Grammar

Misplaced Modifiers
Item 26

Misplaced modifiers can lead to a misreading of a sentence. If a word or phrase or clause is not placed as closely as possible to the words it modifies, the reader can become confused and misinterpret your idea. A sentence or part of a sentence can be ambiguous if modifiers are put in the wrong places. You must take care to place modifiers in their proper places.

1

Words that are modifiers can be misplaced and create confusion.

Consider this sentence:

The people who saw the movie frequently praised it.

The difficulty here is that the word **frequently** comes between **saw the movie** and **praised it**; the word **frequently** could modify either of these phrases. This sentence could be reworded as follows:

The people who frequently saw the movie praised it.
(**Frequently** in this position must apply to **saw**.)

The people who saw the movie praised it frequently.
(In this position, **frequently** must apply to **praised**.)

Consider this second example:

The crowd moved back and forth constantly viewing the lion tamer.

The difficulty here is similar to the previous example. The word **constantly** comes between **moved back and forth** and **viewing the lion tamer**; the word **constantly** could modify either of these phrases. This sentence may be reworded as follows:

The crowd constantly moved back and forth viewing the lion tamer.
(**Constantly** in this position must apply to **moved back and forth**.)

The crowd moved back and forth viewing constantly the lion tamer.
(In this position, **constantly** must apply to **viewing**.)

2

Phrases and clauses as modifiers can be misplaced and create confusion.

Consider this sentence:

I saw the girl in the car that moved.

Was it the girl that moved or the car that moved? **That moved** is unclear because **that** can refer to people or things. The following revisions, however, are clear:

I saw the girl in the car who moved.   OR   I saw the girl who moved in the car. (Either sentence is clearer because **who** can refer only to people, not to things.)

I saw the girl in the car which moved. (**Which** can refer only to things, not to people.)

3

Often only a very slight change can make the difference between an ambiguous sentence and one that is not ambiguous.

The first of the following pair of sentences is unclear; the second is clear.

The waves washed the boat on the shore. (Is the boat on shore already or is it washed up on shore?)

The waves washed the boat onto the shore. (The meaning is clearer.)

Sometimes, however, a greater modification in structure is required. Such a change may correct other faults in addition to ambiguity. The following sentence is not only ambiguous but also wordy.

He took the book in the car that is blue.

Misplaced Modifiers

In this sentence you can assume that **that is blue** modifies **car** because of its position. However, since **that** refers to things, there is a possibility of the clause modifying **book** as well. Either meaning may be expressed clearly in a simpler sentence.

He took the blue book in the car.

OR

He took the book in the blue car.

Misplaced Modifiers—Exercise **1**

Placement of Modifiers

NAME _____

Each of the following sentences contains an underlined phrase that is misplaced. Consider where you should place each phrase so that the writer's meaning is clear. Take the clue from the material in parentheses following each sentence and rewrite the sentence.

EXAMPLE: The children were so hungry that they <u>almost</u> ate all the cookies.
(to modify <u>cookies</u>)
The children were so hungry that they ate <u>almost</u> all the cookies.

1. The general showed how battles are often lost <u>in a series of lectures</u>. (to modify <u>showed</u>)

2. She had two large albums showing pictures of her family <u>hidden in the basement</u>. (to modify <u>albums</u>)

3. I chose the black horse for my sister <u>with the good temper</u>. (to modify <u>black horse</u>)

4. There was one course that showed students how to set off crude bombs <u>at the university</u>. (to modify <u>course</u>)

5. The old man found a green toad <u>searching in the grass for his glasses</u>. (to modify <u>the old man</u>)

6. We saw the child with the bag of candy <u>that was attractive</u>. (to modify <u>the child</u>)

7. She spoke to the boy <u>with a warm smile</u>. (to modify <u>She</u>)

8. She decided to send the shirts to the cleaners <u>that were dirty</u>. (to modify <u>shirts</u>)

Misplaced Modifiers

9. The garden was cleared by the boy scout troop <u>which was overgrown with weeds</u>. (to modify <u>garden</u>)

10. He arrived accompanied by a German shepherd <u>with a big smile on his face</u>. (to modify <u>He</u>)

Ambiguous Sentences

Misplaced Modifiers—Exercise 2

Placement of Modifiers

NAME _____

Each of the following sentences contains an underlined word or phrase that is misplaced. Consider where you should place each phrase or word so that the writer's meaning is clear. Take the clue from the material in parentheses following each sentence and rewrite the sentence.

1. Magazines are read by adults that have dirty words. (to modify magazines)

2. The sixth graders watched patiently waiting for the principal. (to modify waiting)

3. Martin met Stan in the hallway looking for his misplaced cap. (to modify Stan)

4. While she was cleaning the stove, the kitten ran past the maid. (to modify the maid)

5. The woods were full of critters with deep, dark shadows. (to modify woods)

6. Martha sifted the flour carefully preparing the apple pie. (to modify preparing)

7. The greenhouses attracted giant spiders which were transparent. (to modify greenhouses)

8. The mother rocked the baby gently singing him to sleep. (to modify rocked)

9. The policemen caught the young criminals who ran past the grocery. (to modify policemen)

Misplaced Modifiers

10. The split-pea soup tasted good to the lady <u>in the black pot</u>. (to modify <u>split-pea soup</u>)

11. College prepares students for a career <u>while still working</u>. (to modify <u>students</u>)

12. She <u>only</u> had left a pair of slippers. (to modify <u>a pair of slippers</u>)

13. George gave the book of Shakespeare's plays to Marilyn <u>from the library</u>. (to modify <u>book</u>)

14. The doctor prescribed aspirin for the patient <u>in the white coat</u>. (to modify <u>doctor</u>)

15. The kitten was chased by the dog <u>that was black and white</u>. (to modify <u>kitten</u>)

Misplaced Modifiers—Exercise **3**

Placement of Modifiers

NAME _____

Remember that modifiers should be placed close to the words they modify. Complete the following sentences by placing the italicized phrases in positions that point clearly to what they modify. State the writer's intention in parentheses following the sentences. If necessary, rewrite the sentences.

EXAMPLE: *which were delicacies*
The mushrooms _____ were mixed with the carrots _____.
(to modify *mushrooms*)
The mushrooms *which were delicacies* were mixed with the carrots.

1. *who was sitting on the bench*

The daughter _____ was waiting for her mother

_____.

( )

2. *wearing a green button*

Each new salesman _____ sold a used car _____.

( )

3. *waiting in the rain*

The students _____ finally boarded the school bus

_____.

( )

4. *in Milan, Michigan*

Fathers and sons _____ cheered at the banquet _____.

( )

Misplaced Modifiers

5. *carrying bread crumbs*

The ants _____ crawled over the man _____.

(   )

6. *with four apple pies*

Jane and Fred _____ went _____ to

the county fair _____.

(   )

7. *who were underpaid*

In 1976, the workers _____ gathered in protest with

their supervisors _____.

(   )

8. *who thought there would be a tip*

The young waitress _____ helped the salesman

_____.

(   )

9. *with a real estate broker*

The Smiths found _____ their new home _____.

(   )

10. *which usually stayed in the barn*

The birds _____ chirped in the trees _____.

(   )

Grammar

Parallelism
Item 27

You should preserve parallel structure by using units of the same grammatical kind. The principle governing parallelism is that a pair or series of coordinate units should be of the same kind—nouns with nouns, adjectives with adjectives, phrases with phrases, and so on—not a mixture of nouns and phrases. A breakdown in parallelism destroys coherence because it disrupts the reader's expectation started by a series beginning with one kind of unit and shifting to another.

1

When a parallel structure involves single words, make certain they are of the same grammatical kind. Note the faults in the following sentences and how they are corrected.

INCORRECT: The old beliefs about theft have been rejected as **superstitions** [NOUN] and **detrimental** [ADJECTIVE] to one's prestige.

CORRECT: The old beliefs about theft have been rejected as **superstitious** [ADJECTIVE] and **detrimental** [ADJECTIVE] to one's prestige.

INCORRECT: He was a **miser** [NOUN], a **bachelor** [NOUN], and **egotistical.** [ADJECTIVE]

CORRECT: He was a **miser** [NOUN], a **bachelor** [NOUN], and an **egotist** [NOUN].

Parallelism

2

The same principle applies to the use of phrases within a sentence. The phrases should be of the same kind—prepositional phrases with prepositional phrases, infinitive phrases with infinitive phrases—not infinitive phrase with prepositional phrase. Note the following example:

PREPOSITIONAL PHRASE   INFINITIVE

INCORRECT: I enjoy reading simply **for personal enlightenment** and **to develop** PHRASE
mental sharpness.

INFINITIVE PHRASE   INFINITIVE

CORRECT: I enjoy reading simply **to enlighten myself** and **to develop mental** PHRASE
sharpness.

3

Again, the parallel principle applies to pairs of clauses. Most often an error in this category is made when clauses and phrases are mixed. Note the following example:

PREPOSITIONAL PHRASE

INCORRECT: The President commended the steelworkers **for their patriotism** and
ADVERB CLAUSE
because they did not ask for a wage increase.

ADVERB CLAUSE

CORRECT: The President commended the steelworkers **because they were pa-**
ADVERB CLAUSE
triotic and **because they did not ask for a wage increase.**

4

Finally, the parallel principle applies to the use of correlative conjunctions: **either** . . . **or; neither** . . . **nor; not only** . . . **but also**. The grammatical structure must be the same on the right side of both conjunctions. Note the following example:

VERB   OBJECT   NOUN

INCORRECT: The admen not only **convince the reader that the Continental is a**
CLAUSE   NOUN CLAUSE
luxurious car but also **that the car confers status on its owner**.

Use of the Correlative Conjunctions

9. The new humanities course was offered during the fall semester and being taught by the English and Foreign Language departments.

10. When Maria stepped from the boat she saw the city of Buenos Aires with its people, scents, sounds, and incredibly confusing.

Parallelism

Parallelism—Exercise 2

Analysis of Parallel Structures

NAME _____

Examine the following paragraphs and point out the types of parallel structures. Briefly discuss their effectiveness.

1. Poetry turns all things to loveliness; it exalts the beauty of that which is most beautiful and it adds beauty to that which is most deformed; it marries exaltation and horror, grief and pleasure, eternity and change; it subdues to union under its light yoke, all irreconcilable things. It transmutes all that it touches, and every form moving within the radiance of its presence is changed by wondrous sympathy to an incarnation of the spirit which it breathes; its secret alchemy turns potable gold the poisonous waters which flow from death through life; it strips the veil of familiarity from the world, and lays bare the naked and sleeping beauty which is the spirit of its form.

   (Percy Bysshe Shelley, 1821)

2. These are the times that try men's souls: the summer soldier and the sunshine patriot will in this crisis, shrink from the service of his country; but he that stands it NOW, deserves the love and thanks of man and woman. Tyranny, like hell, is not easily conquered; yet we have this consolation with us, that the harder the conflict, the more glorious the triumph. What we obtain too cheap, we esteem too lightly.

   (Thomas Paine, 1776)

3. Evermore it is the order of nature to grow, and every soul is by this intrinsic necessity quitting its whole system of things, its friends and home and laws and faith, as the shell fish crawls out of its beautiful but stony case, because it no longer admits of its growth, and slowly forms a new house.

   (Ralph Waldo Emerson, 1841)

Use of the Correlative Conjunctions

Parallelism—Exercise 3

Completing Parallel Structures

NAME _____

Complete the following paragraph by filling in the blanks with correct parallel structures. Label your structures.

The life of John Smith was not only <u>traumatic</u> but also _____.

During his childhood he was <u>wild</u>, _____, and _____.

However, as he reached his teenage years, he changed to a person <u>with a</u>

<u>sense of direction</u>, _____, and also _____. Many people

saw John as <u>being alone</u> and _____ during his adulthood. And now

that he has died leaving behind no family or friends, John is only slightly re-

membered as a man <u>who found himself</u>, _____, and one _____.

Grammar

Sentence Fragments
Item 29

1

Common types of fragments

A sentence fragment can be defined as a string of words, between an initial capital letter and a period or question mark, that lacks a subject or a finite-verb predicate (or both). A fragment also can occur when the writer does not recognize the difference between independent and dependent clauses. In the case of a dependent clause, the string of words has a subject and a predicate, but it is made dependent (subordinate) by the subordinating conjunction or the relative pronoun at the head of the string. The dependent clause lacks the criterion of presenting a **complete** thought because its completion is **dependent** on an independent clause. Thus, a dependent clause cannot stand by itself as a complete sentence; it is a fragment. Notice the following examples of commonly found fragments.

COMMON TYPES OF FRAGMENTS

1. Appositive phrase: The only type of administrator that we want is one with honesty. **A man who will tell the truth**. (lacks a predicate)

      corrected   The only kind of administrator that we want is one with honesty, a man who will tell the truth.

2. Prepositional phrase: Bill tried to climb Mt. Everest, but it was too difficult. **With the winter snow and ice**. (lacks subject and predicate)

      corrected   Bill tried to climb Mt. Everest, but it was too difficult with the winter snow and ice.

3. Participle phrase:

The concert was exciting because of the rock group. **Running around, jumping off stage, and playing their instruments loudly.** (lacks subject and predicate)

corrected

The concert was exciting because of the rock group running around, jumping off stage, and playing their instruments loudly.

4. Infinitive phrase:

After the semester was over, I had only one idea in mind. **To go to the beach and bask in the sun.** (lacks subject and predicate)

corrected

After the semester was over, I had only one idea in mind: to go to the beach and bask in the sun.

5. Dependent clause:

Randy baked in the hot sun, broiling both sides of his body. **Until he realized that he was overdoing it.** (has a subject and a predicate but is subordinated, made dependent by the **until**)

corrected

Randy baked in the hot sun, broiling both sides of his body, until he realized that he was overdoing it.

6. Fragment with a relative pronoun:

After looking for three weeks, Marsha finally found a room to rent. **That suited exactly her purposes for study.** (has a subject and predicate but is subordinated, made dependent by the relative pronoun **that**)

corrected

After looking for three weeks, Marsha finally found a room to rent that suited exactly her purposes for study.

Sentence Fragments

Sentence Fragments—Exercise 1

Fragments

NAME _____

Identify each of the following as either a sentence or a fragment. If it is not a sentence, perform the necessary corrections to make it one.

EXAMPLE: When I go home for vacation.   FRAGMENT
            When I go home for vacation, I will study.

1. Whenever Fred leaves.

2. Running the final race.

3. Where you see the dogs playing.

4. That old man is crazy.

5. That I must not worry.

6. Sometimes they visit here.

7. If you want to succeed in business without spending too much time.

8. To have dinner early.

9. As if he never wanted to hear it again.

10. Whether Canadians wanted it or not.

11. In order to win the scholarship.

12. When the earthquake occurred and the people left.

13. The children had nightmares about snakes.

14. Before the tulips bloomed and the trees budded.

15. While the tourists waited behind and the guide went into the hotel.

2

The following words and phrases often signal fragments which are dependent clauses. Be sure to double-check sentences beginning with these to make certain they are complete sentences.

WORDS THAT OFTEN BEGIN ADVERB CLAUSES:

after	than
although	though
as, as if, as long, as though	unless
because	until
before	whatever
if	when, whenever
in order that	where, wherever
since	whether
so that	while

WORDS THAT OFTEN BEGIN ADJECTIVE CLAUSES:

that	who
when	whom
where	whose
which	

WORDS THAT OFTEN BEGIN NOUN CLAUSES:

how	whatever
if	when
that	where
what	whether
whichever	why
whoever	
whomever	

Sentence Fragments

Sentence Fragments—Exercise 2

Fragments

NAME _____

Identify each of the following as either a sentence or a fragment. If it is not a sentence, perform the necessary corrections to make it one.

EXAMPLE: When I go home for vacation._____FRAGMENT_____
               When I go home for vacation, <u>I will study</u>.

1. Begging all the time.

2. Whatever Jane says.

3. Although Kip doesn't eat much.

4. Let them be.

5. What I saw.

6. With a pug nose and big feet.

7. Underneath the plum tree, sitting in the breeze.

8. What are you doing?

9. I don't know.

10. Until it snows.

11. Jumping up and down.

12. Sometime I'll go.

13. They don't really dance.

14. Before you leave here.

15. That's disgusting.

Sentence Fragments—Exercise 3

Fragments

NAME _____

Some of the following are not sentences. When you locate a fragment, identify what is causing the fragment and correct it.

EXAMPLE: Although Janice and Mary were together at the movies and then at the party.
FRAGMENT—It is a dependent clause.
Although Janice and Mary were together at the movies and then at the party, **they were still angry with each other**.

1. Many people think that jogging is good for you. Although some doctors have proven that jogging can be harmful to older adults just beginning.

2. Too many students try to drop their English classes.

3. To prepare for the final exams. George studied history, English, and sociology at least ten hours a day.

4. Jill doesn't know what to do. If Jack doesn't come home exactly at five o'clock.

5. The young girl, who has short blond hair and who is always talking to the mail clerk.

6. Don't get me upset. I have to present this paper at 1:00. And be at a cocktail party at 4:00.

7. I really don't see how she's going to be able to race. Limping around the way she is.

Sentence Fragments

8. Most men want to marry someone who is supportive and kind. A woman who will take care of their needs and be good to them.

9. Get out of here! You were the one who insulted my mother. After she accidentally broke one of your glasses.

10. Trying to act concerned. She didn't really deceive any members of the committee.

Sentence Fragments—Exercise **4**

Proofreading for Fragments

NAME _____

Correct the following paragraph by finding and incorporating the fragments properly. (8 fragments)

The class discussion on Jean-Paul Sartre's *Being and Nothingness* proved exciting and productive. As the instructor allowed students to present their own views about existential existence. Linda indicated that she just couldn't believe all that "bunk." Because of her strict Catholic upbringing. Although Frank was hesitant to admit it. He finally said that maybe there's something to what Sartre proposes. Which is applicable to modern society. All the class members readily accepted the difficulty of Sartre's philosophy. When read for an introductory philosophy course. Getting an education. The instructor said, should not be an easy task. Since one will use it the rest of his life. Everyone agreed.

Grammar

Comma Splice and Fused Sentence

Items 30 and 31

1

Fused sentences are not as common in writing as are comma splices. But when they do occur, they are even more of a stumbling block than comma splices are, because the main ideas are not separated to allow the reader to distinguish between two ideas. Instead, readers have to stumble through the "sentence" several times and try to create their own meaning of the ideas. Note the example of a fused sentence below:

INCORRECT: Two suspects were arrested last week one of them was blind.

2

A comma splice occurs when independent clauses are joined with a comma only. This structure always occurs in compound sentences. A comma splice is not only an error in grammar but also an error in punctuation. See the example below:

INCORRECT: Two suspects were arrested last week, one of them was blind.

3

Both fused sentences and comma splices can be remedied in the following ways.

A. Independent clauses can be joined by a coordinate conjunction (**and**, **but**, **or**, **for**, **nor**, **yet**, **so**) with a comma before the conjunction.

CORRECT: Two suspects were arrested last week, and one of them was blind.

B. Or independent clauses can be joined by a semicolon. When a semicolon is used, it must have independent clauses on both sides of it. (See Items 66 and 67 on the use of the semicolon.)

CORRECT: Two suspects were arrested last week; one of them was blind.

C. Or independent clauses can be joined by subordinating one of the independent clauses, using a subordinating conjunction or a relative pronoun.

Some subordinate conjunctions

after	how	unless
although	if	until
as	in order that	what
as if	provided that	whatever
as far as	since	when
as long as	so that	whenever
as soon as	that	where
because	though	wherever
before		whether
		while
		why

Relative pronouns

that
which
who
whoever
whom
whomever

CORRECT: Two suspects were arrested last week because one of them was blind.

D. Finally, a comma splice or fused sentence can be corrected by simply making two sentences of the independent clauses.

CORRECT: Two suspects were arrested last week. One of them was blind.

Comma Splice and Fused Sentence

Comma Splice and Fused Sentence—Exercise 1

Correcting Fused Sentences and Comma Splices

NAME _____

All of the following sentences are either fused sentences or comma splices. Indicate whether each item is either a fused sentence or a comma splice, and correct it, using one of the previously mentioned solutions.

1. Margaret, Debby, and George found Derek in the library, he was reading *Walden.*

2. The hounds ran over the shrubs, around the pond, and into the woods, the rabbit had no chance at all.

3. Up to the government building marched the union protestors, singing and shouting they ended the march.

4. After the game, the team rested on the sidelines some drank lemonade.

5. The psychiatrist listened carefully for many hours the patient talked.

6. Later in the day they rode horses the sun set slowly.

7. Everyone ate quickly, after the play they fell asleep.

8. Long after dawn the fog held tight to the mountain tops, it hugged the crags.

9. Come home with me, give me your hand you are my friend.

10. The deer ran in front of the car the brakes screeched, Rachel screamed.

Comma Splices and Fused Sentences—Exercise **2**

Recognizing Fused Sentences and Comma Splices

NAME _____

Some of the following sentences are correct. If they are, then place a C next to that sentence. If, however, they are incorrect, make the necessary changes, using one of the four solutions.

1. Bob went home. Linda stayed with Mary, and Frank left the country.

2. The faculty voted Millie the scholarship money, after the meeting was over she resigned from the organization.

3. The boy deflated the tires of his brother's bicycle all by himself, his father reinflated them.

4. The angry Indians chased the cavalry far across the mountains, before dawn the cavalry regrouped and attacked.

5. Write carefully and clearly indent paragraphs punctuate as necessary.

6. Uncle Sam needs you; you need Uncle Sam.

7. He started the motorboat and rode quickly after his brother, the boat took him rapidly out of sight into the sun it sank suddenly hiding the disappearing silhouette.

8. The city was confusing with its sights and sounds Roberta was unprepared for this excitement.

9. The storm destroyed all before it and left the people sobbing in the mud.

10. The fire truck reached the fire too late, the house burned down. The embers glowed all night.

Comma Splice and Fused Sentence

Comma Splices and Fused Sentences—Exercise 3

Proofreading for Fused Sentences and Comma Splices

NAME _____

In the paragraph below you will find a given number of fused sentences and comma splices. Correct them with the necessary punctuation and conjunctions.

The women of today are a larger portion of the work force than women of fifty years ago, and thus have more say-so in the future of American society. Today's women are not content to stay home taking care of domestic chores they want to get involved in community services, to pursue full-time careers, and to be a part of growing America. The women of today contribute a great deal to the development of a better society, through their efforts to protect their own consumer interests, they help all of America's purchasing population. They demand better health facilities, the young, middle-aged, and the elderly all benefit. Women's efforts in presenting competency in public office have helped revivify the importance of the democratic ideal, this helps pave the way for future citizens. All in all modern women have created a better society in which to live men have helped too.

(Have you found two fused sentences and three comma splices?)

Grammar

Confusing Sentences
Item 32 (See also Item 45)

A confused sentence is one whose meaning is unclear or scrambled because of some flaw in word choice or arrangement of words. Such a sentence might be called "non-English" because it violates the rules and conventions of the English language: word choice is incompatible or inappropriate for a certain context; sentences do not follow conventional English sentence patterns. Incompatible words or improper arrangement of words often leads to confusion in meaning which cannot be clarified without knowing the writer's intention.

For example, note the following sentence whose meaning is confusing because of incompatible word choice. Pay attention to the underlined words and phrases.

One aspect of morality is your **beliefs** in premarital sex.

The question is whether the writer is talking about only one aspect of a person's morality or about several aspects of one's feelings about premarital sex. The confusion results when the writer links, by use of verb BE, a singular idea (**One aspect**) with a plural idea (**beliefs**). These words are incompatible because one is singular and the other is plural. In this context they both must be singular (**One aspect of morality is your belief** . . .) or plural (**Some aspects of morality are your beliefs** . . .).

The following example is confusing because the arrangement of words gives the impression that some important link is missing. Thus, the reader is unsure of the meaning.

Early in the day, the bus full of people the tour left for San Francisco.

Confusing Sentences

Confusion results in not knowing the link between **the bus full of people** and **the tour**. The conventional word arrangement could link **the tour** to some other element in the sentence by use of a preposition. The following revisions clarify the sentence's meaning:

Early in the day, the bus full of people left on a San Francisco tour.

OR

Early in the day, the bus full of people on the tour left for San Francisco.

Confusing Sentences—Exercise 1

Revising Confusing Sentences

NAME _____

Rewrite the following confusing sentences in two ways that will clarify possible meanings. After each revision, explain the meanings that you were trying to convey.

1. After several minutes of reeling, the fish came to the surface.

2. The visible comparison of one minority group to another exempt from life's conflicts in so much as the individual's ideas, moral, and beliefs are concerned.

3. Another disorder is the state of characters of whom are strewn about in disarray.

4. For example, loneliness to a person can mean being on a crowded street with ten to twenty people standing there with him on that one, single street corner.

5. I feel that maybe the reason this is that God felt this was needed to set His people up establishing and keeping His covenant with His people Israel.

6. Social attitudes were directed toward righteous people which projected an immaculate-type society.

7. Until the final remark by Oliver, does the mood of the story pick up again.

Confusing Sentences

8. An individual wanting to move himself from one stature in life to another is regarded as gratification rather than it being regarded as it was in medieval times.

9. The events of *Portrait of a Lady*, Isabel relates to us, appears from a different light than from her ideas when she was younger.

10. Upon entering the room the thing that grabs your attention are all the desks cluttered around the room.

11. College is an atmosphere for adults.

12. Whether the poem is successful or not is extremely difficult to do.

13. Not necessarily does he need to be directly in focus with it, but as a member of society, he is concerned with himself as a member of society, he concerned and mainly nothing else.

14. Reds are aliens under the suspicion of sympathy with the Communist régime.

15. It was 7:45 that morning—a morning I will always remember as being drenched with fear and emotion.

Grammar

Verb Forms
Item 33

Although many errors involving verbs result from the lack of agreement between subject and predicate (see Item 22), verb errors also occur because of improper past-tense and past-participle forms. This problem is particularly troublesome when verb tenses shift in paragraphs; the reader can misinterpret easily the chronological organization.

The basic rule regarding past-tense and past-participle forms of regular verbs is that they are formed by adding *-ed*, *-d*, or *-t* to the verb stem (e.g., walk—walked, believe—believed, build—built). In cases where you are unsure of a past-tense or past-participle form of an irregular verb, you should consult a dictionary. For your reference a list of the most often used irregular verbs and their past-tense and past-participle forms follows.

STEM FORM	PAST TENSE	PAST PARTICIPLE
begin	began	begun
bite	bit	bitten
blow	blew	blown
break	broke	broken
choose	chose	chosen
do	did	done
drink	drank	drunk
drive	drove	driven
eat	ate	eaten
fall	fell	fallen
fly	flew	flown
forget	forgot	forgotten
give	gave	given

Verb Forms

STEM FORM	PAST TENSE	PAST PARTICIPLE
go	went	gone
know	knew	known
lay	laid	laid
lie	lay	lain
pay	paid	paid
ride	rode	ridden
ring	rang	rung
rise	rose	risen
run	ran	run
see	saw	seen
sit	sat	sat
speak	spoke	spoken
swear	swore	sworn
take	took	taken
throw	threw	thrown
wear	wore	worn

Verb Forms—Exercise 1

Correcting Verb Forms

NAME _____

Correct the main verbs in the following sentences for past-tense and past-participle forms. Underline the incorrect verb and write the correction above. If you are uncertain about a form, consult the preceding list of irregular verbs or a dictionary.

1. The women's organization was not use to being ignored by the senator.

2. Before the campers come upon shelter, they almost drownded.

3. There was four children on the playground, and they had come with their teacher.

4. Mona and Fred were suppose to pick up their daughter at 5:30, but their daughter had left because she was use to being picked up at 5:00.

5. The brown dog who had bit the mailman was being protected by the humane society.

6. All of the first graders had drank their daily ration of milk.

7. The worn-out jogger laid on the couch for hours after the race.

8. He use to play soccer in South America before he was recruited by the NFL.

9. Their feet were nearly froze from the hike in subzero weather.

10. The new dress had been wore only three times before the seams gave out.

11. The volleyball team had chose Marsha as the new captain.

12. On Friday, January 18, I received a call from my neighbor's lawyer saying that I'm being sued and was to give a statement to the insurance company.

13. The Atlanta tour had went from Florida to Georgia in record time.

14. The defendant was swore in as a witness while the jury looks on.

15. The sun rose above the Atlantic fog, just as it always has rose.

Verb Forms

Proofreading for Verb Tense

NAME _____

Proofread the following paragraph making certain that past-tense and past-participle forms are correct. When you find an incorrect verb form, underline the incorrect verb and write the correction above.

The University basketball team's loss to College at the beginning of the season is the

final straw for Coach Brown, and the team knew it. Having been beat mercilessly,

the team members at first were embarrassed but later come to realize their faults.

When they finally recognized that they pass the ball without accuracy, that they take

low percentage shots, and that they lacked team coordination, they vowed to im-

prove their weaknesses. Coach Brown was thankful that the team members came

to their senses. The plan for improvement starts with practice. They worked hard.

They practice their shooting and passing. During their final games, they learned to

play selflessly; they learn that team effort was the best way to win a game.

Verb Forms—Exercise **3**

Verb Tense

NAME _____

Starting with one of the phrases or clauses below, write a paragraph in which you use past-tense and past-participle forms. If you are uncertain about a form be sure to consult a dictionary.

1. When I was twelve years old . . .

2. During World War II . . .

3. My father told us that when he was growing up . . .

4. The antiwar rallies of the '60s . . .

5. The first American moon landing . . .

Style

Sentence Variety

By varying sentence structure, a writer can create more readable and interesting prose. Sentence variety can be achieved by rearranging the verbal elements in a sentence (its surface structure) while maintaining the basic meaning (its deep structure). In order to see the possibilities for various structures, writers must be clear about their intentions and the meaning in sentences. By identifying kernel sentences, those sentences whose deep structure and surface structure are the simplest possible, writers can begin to manipulate the structures, producing sentences with clear emphasis and appropriate tone.

There are four basic transformations which allow writers to recreate sentences in a variety of patterns: combining (compounding), embedding (subordinating), shifting (rearranging), deleting (omitting). Any one or a combination of these methods can produce sentences that are less monotonous and more appealing. In each particular case, however, the writer's judgment about which sentence most effectively presents the intended meaning will determine the method(s) used.

Note the ways in which the following kernel sentences can be combined into one new sentence with clearer emphasis and less wordiness.

	1. The museum purchased a painting.
KERNEL SENTENCES	2. · The painting was rare.
	3. The director of the museum was pleased.

Step 1   Kernel sentences 1 and 2 can be combined so that kernel sentence 2 will modify **painting** in kernel sentence 1.

The museum purchased a painting which was rare.

                    OR

The museum purchased a rare painting.

74

In both combinations, kernel sentence 2 modifies **painting** in kernel sentence 1. In the first combination, the relative clause **which was rare** modifies **painting**; in the second combination, by the process of deletion, the adjective **rare** modifies **painting**.

Step 2   The sentence resulting from the second combination in Step 1 can be combined with kernel sentence 3.

The museum purchased a rare painting, and the director of the museum was pleased.

The coordinate conjunction **and** combines the two sentences into one compound sentence. Another way to combine the sentences into a compound sentence is as follows:

The museum purchased a rare painting; therefore, the director of the museum was pleased.

Here the sentences are combined by use of the conjunctive adverb **therefore**, making a compound sentence. Yet another combination might be as follows:

The director of the museum was pleased because the museum purchased a rare painting.

Here the original kernel sentences are rearranged into a complex sentence by use of the subordinating conjunction **because**.

Sentence Variety

Sentence Variety—Exercise 1

Combining Sentences

NAME _____

Using the techniques described above, combine the following groups of kernel sentences. Make as many combinations as possible and consider the different emphasis in each combination.

1. The plane crashed.
   The crash was in Wyoming.

2. Rona was at the track meet.
   Rona was a timekeeper.

3. The fire raged.
   The fire was out of control.
   The firefighters were frightened.

4. The book is red.
   The title is *Paradise Lost*.
   The book is in the library.

5. The teacher made the assignment.
   The assignment was for a composition class.
   The assignment was due on Friday.

6. Peter cast his fly.
   Peter cast into the stream.
   Peter snagged his line.
   The line was on a bush.

7. Janet walked along the path.
Jim walked along the path.
The path was moonlit.
The path was in the woods.

8. Jed was on the football team.
Jed was the quarterback.
The football team lost games.
The football team won one game.

9. Fourteen high school students went to New York City.
Two chaperones went to New York City.
New York City is an exciting place.
Millions of people live in New York City.

10. The tanker ship sped through the waves.
The waves were twenty feet high.
The wind howled.
The thunder was frightening.
The lightning was frightening.

Sentence Variety

Combining Sentences

NAME _____

Using the techniques described above, combine the following groups of kernel sentences. Then group the combined sentences into one paragraph rearranging the sentences, if necessary, to make the paragraph coherent.

1. The aliens entered the *Enterprise.*
The aliens came through cracks.
The cracks were in the engine room.

2. Captain Kirk commands the *Enterprise.*
The Captain was surprised.
Captain Kirk saw an alien vessel.

3. Spock listened to the aliens.
Spock interpreted for the aliens.
The aliens wanted to escape.
The escape was to Earth.

4. A Red Alert was necessary.
Battle stations were taken.
The *Enterprise* crew acted without fear.

5. The aliens were humanoid.
The aliens were greenish.
The aliens were transparent.
The aliens appeared three feet tall.
The aliens had a language.
The language had peculiar sounds.

6. Spock was his calm self.
Spock was his usual self.
Spock was able to communicate.
The communication was with the aliens.
The aliens seemed pleased.

Exercise 2 continued

Rearrange the sentences into a coherent paragraph.

Style

Wrong Word and Faulty Predication

Item 40

1

Wrong word

Some words have similar sounds and can be confused easily. Always be sure you have selected the word that has the precise meaning you want. If you are not sure about a word's meaning, look it up in the dictionary before using it in your writing.

2

Unfamiliar words

Words that are unfamiliar can often be misused. Do not use words only because they are big or fine sounding; be sure you know the proper context for any new words you include in your writing.

3

Faulty predication

Faulty predication occurs when the connection between subject and predicate in a sentence is illogical. Subject and predicate should match grammatically and should make good sense.

Precise and Appropriate Words

Items 41 and 42

1

Using precise words

The use of vague or overly general words will make your writing unclear and dull. In order to convey your ideas clearly and exactly, you must choose precise, specific words.

VAGUE: The class came up with some **good** ideas for class projects.
MORE PRECISE: The class came up with some **original but inexpensive** ideas for
               class projects.

In these sentences, notice the difference in meaning made by a change in one precise word.

The pianist **grinned** at his audience.
The pianist **smirked** at his audience.

2

Using appropriate words

A word is used inappropriately if it does not suit its surroundings. Do not mix formal and informal language or introduce words into a sentence that change its tone. Always use words that are consistent with the occasion, the audience, and the mood of your writing.

Precise and Appropriate Words

INAPPROPRIATE: I would like to say that the people of this town have treated m
hospitably, courteously, and **downright neighborly**.

APPROPRIATE: I would like to say that the people of this town have treated m
hospitably, courteously, and **pleasantly**.

INAPPROPRIATE: Today, children, we're going to the museum without taking ou
customary writing implements.

APPROPRIATE: Today, children, we're going to the museum without taking ou
pencils.

Precise and Appropriate Words—Exercise **1**

Precise words

NAME _____

Find two more specific words for each of the following general words.

EXAMPLE: dog   collie   dachshund

1. artist   _____   _____

2. walk (v.)   _____   _____

3. happy   _____   _____

4. plant (n.)   _____   _____

5. look (v.)   _____   _____

Precise and Appropriate Words

Precise and Appropriate Words—Exercise 2

Precise words

NAME _____

In the following sentences replace the underlined vague or overly general words with more specific words.

EXAMPLE: Take that <u>thing</u> out of the kitchen.
Take that <u>frog</u> out of the kitchen.

1. There are <u>some nice things</u> in that department store window.

2. With a little practice, John can play <u>most things</u>.

3. Our room looks much brighter now with <u>all that stuff</u> on the walls.

4. Sally is <u>a good child</u>.

5. Actually, Frank is <u>a very nice guy</u>.

6. The litter on our city streets is a disgrace; we all ought to <u>get out and do something</u>.

7. She's chosen <u>an interesting way</u> to furnish her apartment.

8. David went to see the movie twice because he thought it was <u>so meaningful</u>.

9. When we're together, my sister and I always have <u>a lot of fun</u>.

10. Walking in the hills is <u>a good experience</u>.

Style

Using the Proper Idiom
Item 43

Many expressions in American English, particularly those involving preposi-tions, cannot be understood in terms of the individual meanings of the words. These expressions result from custom in the language and must simply be learned as the unique way native speakers express a particular idea.

In compounded phrases, if a preposition does not fit idiomatically with both elements of the compound, the appropriate preposition for each element must be used.

CORRECT: He likes to read and talk about philosophical issues.
(The preposition **about** fits idiomatically with both **to read** and [to] **talk**.)

CORRECT: No other dessert is better than or equal to my mother's chocolate pie.
(In this sentence, **than** fits with **better** but does not fit with **equal**. There-fore, an appropriate preposition—in this case **to**—must be used with **equal**.)

Using the Proper Idiom

Using the Proper Idiom—Exercise 1

Proper idiom

NAME _____

Rewrite the following sentences, correcting unidiomatic expressions.

1. Advertisements produce much of their effect by making an appeal at people's emotions.

2. I think hamsters are inferior than dogs as pets.

3. In Dr. Adam's class, the study of paragraphing is subsequent and dependent on the study of sentence structure.

4. Shall we meet to Jim's house tonight?

5. Every evening he listens the radio.

6. How long have you been waiting against an answer to your letter?

7. Will you introduce me with your mother?

8. The orchestra began to playing a rousing march.

9. My father succeeded to learn Italian at the age of eighty-two.

10. He's certainly capable to murder anyone he hated.

Using the Proper Idiom—Exercise **2**

Proper idiom

NAME _____

Indicate the prepositions that can be used idiomatically with the following words. Then use each phrase in a sentence.

EXAMPLE: comply—comply with
                   You must comply with many safety regulations when you install
                   a wood-burning stove.

1. refer—

2. different—

3. in proportion—

4. similar—

5. associate (v.)—

6. disassociate—

Using the Proper Idiom

NAME _____

Some common verbs can express a number of different meanings, depending on the prepositions following them. For each word here give two prepositions that influence its meaning and use each in a sentence.

EXAMPLE: shut
            shut up—"Shut up," he said, "you're talking too much."
            shut down—The factory was forced to shut down during the
                       strike.

1. run—

2. pass—

3. take—

4. turn—

5. call—

Trite Expressions—Exercise 2

Eliminating trite expressions

NAME _____

In the following sentences, underline the trite expressions and replace them with original and interesting phrases.

EXAMPLE: It was so quiet in the room, you could <u>hear a pin drop</u>.
It was so quiet in the room, you could hear a mouse sneeze.

1. When Jim saw the bear, he ran as fast as his legs would carry him.

2. John saw the gigantic bat and turned white as a sheet.

3. You'd better not eat all that cake, unless you want to be fat as a pig.

4. With their courageous ascent of the peak, the climbers covered themselves with glory.

5. It's sad but true that most people procrastinate.

Trite Expressions

Eliminating trite expressions

NAME _____

Write five sentences containing phrases that you often overuse. Rewrite the sentences to eliminate the trite phrases or replace them with fresher ones.

1.

2.

3.

4.

5.

Style

Awkward Sentences
Item 45

Although they may be grammatically correct, awkward sentences are clumsy and difficult to understand. They generally result from one or more of three types of fault: (a) unnatural word order, (b) wordy or rambling structures (see also Items 46 and 47, Wordiness and Redundancy), (c) successions of rhyming words. Often awkwardly written sentences can be identified when they are read aloud. They then can be corrected to a form the writer would use if speaking the sentence out loud.

1

Unnatural word order

Words and phrases should appear in a sentence in an order that is natural and followed easily. Do not needlessly separate modifiers from the words they modify or split phrases that form a unit of thought in a sentence.

AWKWARD: Almost, in the accident, John was killed.
IMPROVED: John was almost killed in the accident.

AWKWARD: Dr. Jones always has time for, no matter how busy she may be, students who want to see her.
IMPROVED: No matter how busy she may be, Dr. Jones always has time for students who want to see her.

Awkward Sentences

2

Rambling or wordy structures

A rambling sentence contains long strings of phrases and clauses or uses more words than necessary to convey an idea clearly. Since this excess material distracts from the main idea of the sentence, it is best to eliminate unnecessary words and phrases and to form two or more sentences from one long, rambling sentence.

AWKWARD: As I was walking home, I met my aunt in front of Jones' Grocery, which is the best place in town to buy cheese because they have all different kinds of foreign and domestic cheeses at reasonable prices.

IMPROVED: As I was walking home, I met my aunt in front of Jones' Grocery. That is the best place in town to buy cheese because they have all different kinds of foreign and domestic cheeses at reasonable prices.

3

Unintentional rhyme

If a sentence contains several words that rhyme, those words will stand out because of their sound and will distract attention from the idea the sentence is expressing. Replace rhyming words with synonyms that do not rhyme.

AWKWARD: We could do **away** with the refuse problem in the **bay today**, if the citizens would **say** "yes" to bond issue 53.

IMPROVED: We could eliminate the refuse problem in the bay immediately, if the citizens would only vote "yes" to bond issue 53.

Awkward Sentences—Exercise **1**

Unnatural word order

NAME _____

Rewrite the following sentences to correct unnatural word order.

1. To study on the lawn or under the trees, the children left, whenever they wanted to, their schoolroom.

2. We walked down the path slowly bordered by tall firs.

3. She expects to, even though it will be difficult, in three years complete her college course.

4. Almost, they were ready to, when we came, go with us.

5. Very few, only those of grammar and spelling, rules apply to news writing.

Awkward Sentences

Awkward Sentences—Exercise 2

Rambling structures

NAME _____

Rewrite the following rambling sentences so that they are clear and coherent.

1. Around my home town there are ranges of hills like those in West Virginia where I spent a vacation once on my grandfather's farm when I was twelve.

2. Dental hygiene, which is a comparatively new field, offers good jobs at a time when jobs are hard to find, so schools that offer courses in dental hygiene are attracting many students.

3. The art of consistent and impassioned argument without personal animosity or belligerence between the opponents is not practiced in the United States, although one often reads about such arguments in contemporary Russian and French novels, and probably those books offer a fairly reliable picture of the social practices in Russia and France, so we must ask ourselves why such arguments do not exist in our country.

4. Because they left the house hastily, they were drenched to the skin because they had left their raincoats behind even though the sky was cloudy and threatened rain.

5. Having a large family was a helpful experience for my cousin because she became a teacher and could deal with children well because she was used to small children and what they needed.

Awkward Sentences—Exercise **3**

Unintentional rhyme

NAME _____

Rewrite the following sentences, underlining awkward rhyming words and replacing them with well-chosen synonyms.

1. I'm amazed at how well her ways of raising rabbits pay.

2. A soft breeze eased through the trees and teased the waters of the pond into ripples.

3. Mr. Hawkins became sage in his old age and seldom flew into the rages he had engaged in when he was younger.

4. For prose writers, my advice is to be concise, use precise language, and avoid the device of rhyme.

5. A closed mind reviews few new ideas.

Style

Wordiness
Items 46 and 47

1

Wordy sentences

Avoid using more words than are necessary to express your ideas; instead, be as direct and concise as possible. A few **well-chosen** words are clearer and more effective than long strings of words that add nothing to the meaning of your sentence. There are two main ways to correct wordy sentences: by omitting all unnecessary words and by restructuring the sentence.

WORDY SENTENCE: The winter snowstorms that occurred in the state of Ohio in the year of 1940 were the worst snowstorms ever recorded in that state.

IMPROVED: The snowstorms that occurred in Ohio in 1940 were the worst ever recorded in that state.

WORDY SENTENCE: Life for the first settlers in the new country held many hardships and privations unknown to those people before they set out from their old homeland.

IMPROVED: The first settlers in the new country experienced many hardships and privations unknown to them before.

2

Redundancy

Redundancy is a specific kind of wordiness, occurring when the same or similar words are repeated unnecessarily.

Wordiness—Exercise 2

Wordy sentences

NAME _____

Correct the wordiness of the following sentences by restructuring them. Do *not* change the basic idea of the sentence.

EXAMPLE: In his career in a real estate office as a realtor, my brother was never very successful or happy, but he was much more successful and happy when he became a carpenter building houses instead of selling them.

REVISION: My brother was much happier and more successful as a carpenter than as a realtor—building houses rather than selling them.

1. My cats, who live with me in my house, often cannot be found, for they know every dark corner and all the small, secret places in the house where they can hide.

2. While young people are going through their early adolescence, they sometimes want to experience the security of childhood, but, at the same time, they want to demonstrate adult initiative and responsibility, too.

3. After we left the state of Colorado, we entered the state of Kansas, and from there on we saw only plains, broad rivers, and low hills; the mountains of Colorado were behind us.

4. Now, especially, it is true that this state needs new leadership in the government and not just new leadership, but good new leadership in both the legislature and the governorship.

5. Paul and Virginia found that traveling all over the world could become routine after a few months and they were both matter-of-fact about what had at first been an exciting adventure for them both.

Wordiness

Wordy sentences

NAME _____

Using both methods of correcting wordiness, rewrite the following paragraph.

In Homer's epic poem the *Iliad*, the form of a warrior-goddess is the one the goddess Athene most often assumes. She appears stern and terrible; her figure strikes fear, awe, and fright into the hearts of the soldiers. She only has to walk into the Achean camp to rouse the soldiers to fierce fighting mettle. Her battle cry terrifies her enemies very much. In this fierce side of her nature, however, there exists in her no brutality or excessive bloodthirstiness, even though she is a fierce warrior. Instead, she is like a general in an army who is implacable in battle, fighting fiercely, yet cool-headed, well versed in strategy, who knows how best to use an army to the best advantage. Athene knows, too, when there is also a time for peace. Thus, she guides the spear of Diomedes against Pandaros and gives Diomedes great prowess in battle by her aid in the fight; she wounds a sister goddess Aphrodite in her fury, but she also counsels with Apollo for an armistice to stop the fighting, and she stops Ares in his quite rash scheme to avenge his son by taking fierce revenge on his son's slayers. Athene is a terrible figure as a warrior-goddess in war, but she is also prudent and a strategist, as mentioned before. In warfare, she knows when to stop fighting.

Style

Mixed Metaphor
Item 48

Metaphor is based on comparison; similar qualities are seen in two different things.

EXAMPLE: Often a person sets out early in life on a sea of possibilities, only to suffer immediate shipwreck in some storm.
(A person's experience is compared to a sea voyage.)

Mixed metaphors occur when the objects of comparison are joined incongruously or inconsistently. Often this is a result of writing in clichés rather than creating fresh images.

EXAMPLE: Often a person sets out early in life on a sea of possibilities, only to strike out immediately.
(It is inconsistent to speak of a sea voyage in terms of baseball. The metaphor is mixed.)

Mixed Metaphor

Mixed Metaphor—Exercise 1

Mixed metaphor

NAME _____

Replace the mixed metaphors in the following sentences with clear consistent metaphors.

EXAMPLE: In the debate, Jim put all his cards on the table, but his opponent threw him a curve.
In the debate, Jim put all his cards on the table, but his opponent had an ace up his sleeve.

1. The disease of jealousy had already stabbed him in the back.

2. It's an uphill climb, trying to keep our balance on the narrow bridge of economic stability.

3. By the time Mark was twenty, he had achieved the pinnacle of success, only to find it was a pig in a poke.

4. His words sprang into her mind like lions and nestled in her heart.

5. The old man had come into safe harbor at last, after leaping all the barriers life had placed before him.

Mixed Metaphor—Exercise 2

Mixed metaphor

NAME _____

Circle the letter of the best completion for each of the following metaphoric statements.

EXAMPLE:　My love is a diamond
       a. that warms my heart.
      ⓑ in whose facets I see all the world reflected.
      c. and my heart the oyster that encloses it.

1. It's better not to wait for opportunity to knock at your door;
   a. you should jump on the bandwagon yourself.
   b. go out to meet it on the road.
   c. grab it on the wing.

2. His anger stormed through his neighbor's arguments
   a. and ricocheted from the wall of his prejudice.
   b. and drowned in his prejudice.
   c. and beat against a solid wall of prejudice.

3. Hope is a faint star
   a. that makes its nest in our hearts.
   b. that leads us when our souls are dark.
   c. with deeps roots in our souls.

4. Ideas planted in careful thought
   a. will not easily be uprooted by the passing winds of popular opinion.
   b. will not easily catch fire from the sparks of popular opinion.
   c. will not be blinded by the glare of popular opinion.

5. I just skated through that exam
   a. and cleared all the bases.
   c. even over the thin ice.
   d. without hitting a single false note.

Mixed Metaphor

Mixed Metaphor—Exercise 3

Mixed metaphor

NAME _____

Compose four sentences containing original and consistent metaphors.

1.

2.

3.

4.

Use of Active and Passive Voice

Item 49

Choice of an active or a passive verb can influence the effect or tone of a sentence. As the names indicate, **active** voice emphasizes the action of the sentence and its performer; **passive** voice emphasizes the receiver of the action. Generally, active verbs are more forceful and direct than passive verbs.

ACTIVE VOICE: In the beginning, God created the heavens and the earth.
PASSIVE VOICE: In the beginning, the heavens and the earth were created by God.

If the receiver of action is more important than the actor, passive voice is the most effective choice to make.

EXAMPLE: Mary is loved by everyone who knows her.
(Here the emphasis is on Mary rather than on the people who know her.)

The passive voice can also suggest detachment or objectivity. Scientific writing often makes use of passive verb forms.

EXAMPLE: My conclusions have been based on data from 406 separate experiments.

Too much use of the passive voice, however, will tend to make your writing tedious and colorless.
Avoid unnecessary switching from one voice to another; this switching is confusing and awkward.

AWKWARD: Jim and I stayed home all day, and many of our chores were finished.
IMPROVED: Jim and I stayed home all day and finished many of our chores.

Use of Active and Passive Voice

Use of Active and Passive Voice—Exercise 1

Use of active and passive voice

NAME _____

Decide whether or not the passive voice has been used effectively in the following sentences. Write *E* after the effective sentences. Rewrite ineffective sentences in the active voice.

EXAMPLE: The dog was chased by the cat.
                   The cat chased the dog.

1. The child was snatched up by its father and carried out of the street.

2. The three businessmen ran wildly down the street, but the bus was missed.

3. A salt is formed by the combination of an acid with a base.

4. The chasm was leaped by the escaping bandit.

5. His house can easily be missed by passers-by; it's a long way back from the road.

6. Safety should be considered before speed.

7. The peas, tomatoes, beets, and squash were grown by me.

8. William Carter was elected mayor by an overwhelming majority.

9. The fox was followed by the hounds, but they lost its scent in the creek.

10. Help! We've been trapped by an enraged porcupine!

Paragraphing

Unity in the Paragraph
Item 50

The paragraph is a group of sentences developing a single main topic, which will often be stated in a topic sentence. Every sentence in the paragraph should contribute to the development of that central idea. If all ideas in a paragraph are related carefully to the topic, the paragraph will be unified.

Clear, definite topic sentences

Unity of the paragraph begins with a clear, definite topic sentence. This sentence should state **exactly** what will be discussed in the paragraph and is often a general statement that will be specified and supported in the rest of the paragraph. The topic sentence may or may not actually appear in the finished paragraph, but it must **always** be present in the mind of the writer. It is a good idea for beginning writers always to include topic sentences in their paragraphs to avoid confusion.

EXAMPLE: In Greek mythology, Athene often appears as a warrior-goddess, stern and terrifying.

This sentence states clearly and definitely the aspects of Athene that will be discussed in the paragraph. No other aspects of the goddess besides her connection with war and her stern, terrifying nature will be relevant to the paragraph.

2

Developing topic sentences

All other sentences in a paragraph will develop the idea of the topic sentence
Nothing should be allowed into the paragraph that is unnecessary or irrele
vant to that idea.

Unity in the Paragraph—Exercise **1**

Clear, definite topic sentences

NAME _____

Identify and underline the vague or unclear parts of the following sentences and rewrite them so that they could be used as topic sentences for paragraphs.

EXAMPLE: Abraham Lincoln was <u>an important man</u>.
(The underlined phrase is vague and undefined.)
REWRITE: Abraham Lincoln brought a sense of integrity and purpose to the presidency at a time when the nation was seriously divided.
(This revision specifies ways in which Lincoln was important. Other definite topic sentences might be composed that state why Lincoln was important.)

1. Comparing a country-western song with a hard-rock song, I find that the country-western song has more meaning than the hard-rock song.
REWRITE:

2. People in our culture have ideas and beliefs that are different from those of another culture.
REWRITE:

3. The book *The Heart of the Matter* was interesting only in some parts.
REWRITE:

4. Television affects people.
REWRITE:

5. Energy is a problem.
REWRITE:

6. There are many aspects to student evaluations.
REWRITE:

7. Life is hard.
REWRITE:

Unity in the Paragraph

8. Today's education isn't working.
REWRITE:

Note to the student: You may have noticed by now that vague, overgeneralized paragraph topics are dull, as well as confusing, both for the writer and the reader of the paragraph.

Unity in the Paragraph—Exercise 2

Identifying topic sentences

NAME _____

Identify and underline the topic sentence in each of the following paragraphs.

1. Game and sport fish are among the most carefully tended and conserved of all natural resources, but the rest of our native fishes receive virtually no attention, and a number have become extinct in recent years or are in danger of extinction. This is especially true of the fresh-water fishes of the southwestern United States, where there is hardly a river or stream that has not been affected by the activities of man. Because aquatic habitats in the desert are isolated for long periods of time, punctuated infrequently by floods, the distribution pattern of the fishes of the Southwest once provided an exceptional opportunity for the study of speciation and zoogeography. Now the pattern has been thoroughly disrupted, often unnecessarily, and if anything like it still exists in the world, it is not in North America.

   (David W. Ehrenfeld, *Biological Conservation*)

2. The human race, as it immediately concerns us, has a vertical axis of about 40,000 years and as of 1900 A.D. a horizontal spread of roughly 3000 different languages and 1000 different cultures. Every living culture and language is the result of countless cross-fertilizations—not a "rise and fall" of civilizations, but more like a flower-like periodic absorbing-blooming-bursting and scattering of seed. Today we are aware as never before of the plurality of human life-styles and possibilities, while at the same time being tied, like in an old silent movie, to a runaway locomotive rushing headlong toward a very singular catastrophe. Science, as far as it is capable of looking "on beauty bare" is on our side. Part of our being modern is the very fact of our awareness that we are one with our beginnings—contemporary with all periods—members of all cultures. The seeds of every social structure or custom are in the mind.

   (Gary Snyder, *Earth House Hold*)

3. In such a day, in September or October, Walden is a perfect forest mirror, set round with stones as precious to my eye if fewer or rarer. Nothing so fair, so pure, and at the same time so large, as a lake, perchance, lies on the surface of the earth. Sky water. It needs no fence. Nations come and go without defiling it. It is a mirror which no stone can crack, whose quicksilver will never wear off, whose gilding Nature continually repairs; no storms, no dust, can dim its surface

Unity in the Paragraph

ever fresh;—a mirror in which all impurity presented to it sinks, swept and dusted
by the sun's hazy brush,—this the light dust-cloth,—which retains no breath that
is breathed on it, but sends its own to float as clouds high above its surface, and
be reflected in its bosom still.

(H. D. Thoreau, *Walden*

Unity in the Paragraph—Exercise **3**

Composing topic sentences

NAME _____

No topic statements appear in the following paragraphs. Compose a topic sentence for each of them, expressing the main idea of the paragraph.

1. You may see from a boat, in calm weather, near the sandy eastern shore, where the water is eight or ten feet deep, and also in some other parts of the pond, circular heaps half a dozen feet in diameter by a foot in height, consisting of small stones less than a hen's egg in size where all around is bare sand. At first you wonder if the Indians could have formed them on the ice for any purpose, and so, when the ice melted, they sank to the bottom; but they are too regular and some of them plainly too fresh for that. They are similar to those found in rivers; but as there are no suckers nor lampreys here, I know not by what fish they could be made. Perhaps they are the nests of the chivin. These lend a pleasing mystery to the bottom.

(H. D. Thoreau, *Walden*)

2. Ten minutes into our morning watch we spotted a finback; he spouted six times at intervals of six to ten seconds; sounded, and was gone. Not until 6:30 P.M. was our day's patience rewarded. Forty or fifty white-sided dolphins, three-quarters of a mile to the west, were soaring and cavorting in the fading light of the evening. In a line nearly a quarter of a mile long, they were strung out, seven-to-nine foot dolphins leaping as high as twice their body length out of the water, twisting, swirling, and whirling with exuberance. Within moments of spotting them, we were joined by Stanley, Richard, and the Chief, who were beginning to feel the magic too.

(Gordon S. Hayward, "A Whalewatchers Diary," *Country Journal*, August 1977)

3. The migrant worker gets up at five A.M., is picked up in a roadside barrio at six A.M. and loaded into a bus, truck, or van with other workers. He is driven five, ten, or thirty miles to the fields to work the day under a hot sun. A break in the midmorning, thirty minutes for lunch, and a ten-minute break in the afternoon provide his only rest periods. He spends the rest of the day either hunched down cutting lettuce, carrying a ladder from one orange tree to another, or picking grapes from the vines. After a ten-hour workday, he is taken back to his desolate barrio.

(James Santibanez, "El Teatro Campesino Today and El Teatro Urbano," *The Chicano*)

Unity in the Paragraph

Unity in the Paragraph—Exercise **4**

Developing topic sentences

NAME _____

Rewrite the following paragraphs so that all the sentences relate to the topic statement. Omit unnecessary statements; add anything that you think is needed to make a unified and complete paragraph.

1. This story was interesting, only in some parts. The parts I really enjoyed were some of the poems; for example, there was a poem on page 296. This story was about Wilson and some other characters. Wilson seemed to like poetry, and he absorbed it secretly like a drug. He never had a car of his own. He felt almost intolerably lonely. He also seemed to talk a lot about Scobie. Scobie was still a novice in the world of deceit; so was Wilson. He hadn't lived in it since childhood, and he felt an odd elderly envy for Scobie, much as an old crook might envy the young crook serving his first sentence to whom all this was new. I also enjoyed the part where they found the diary.

2. Utah is a land of strong contrasts. Forested mountains in the north give way to salt plains, harsh deserts adjoin fertile farm lands, miles of sparsely populated country surround the metropolitan area of Salt Lake City. Perhaps Utah is best known to the traveler for its fruit orchards. In the spring, the countryside is filled with flowering trees. Both the Green River and the Colorado River flow through the state, the one winding down from high Wyoming mountains, the other entering Utah across the western Colorado prairie. These great rivers cut through the southern sandstone desert, forming corridors of vegetation in an arid country. People who tried to navigate these rivers often perished. Salt Lake City is the capital of Utah. It is an industrial center with its steel mills and oil refineries, lying between the mountains on the east and the Great Salt Lake. But agriculture is also a basic part of Utah's economy. The pioneers must have admired this valley, for their first settlement was here. Utah is called the Beehive State.

Unity in the Paragraph—Exercise 5

Developing topic sentences

NAME _____

Choose one of the rewritten topics from Exercise 1 and write your own clear, unified paragraph. The topic sentence should appear somewhere in your paragraph.

Paragraphing

Coherence in the Paragraph
Item 51

1

Coherence in the paragraph

Coherence in the paragraph means that the sentences are so written, arranged, and interlinked that the thought stated in the topic sentence flows smoothly and clearly from one sentence to the next. The reader should be able to follow the development of idea in the paragraph easily and logically, without confusion about the relationship of each sentence to those preceding and following it.

2

Main methods of achieving paragraph coherence

There are two main methods of achieving paragraph coherence:

a. Sentence arrangement. The sentences of the paragraph should be arranged so that each is related to the one that comes before and the one that comes after. This arrangement may be temporal, spatial, or logical (following a pattern such as cause and effect, inductive use of detail to support a general statement, etc.) Parallel sentence structure is also a method of achieving coherence.

b. Transitional words. Transitional or connective words are words that connect the thought of one sentence to that of preceding sentences. These linking words are such words as pronouns, demonstrative adjectives (**this, that, these, those**), conjunctions, or conjunctive adverbs (**however, moreover, also, hence**, and so on).

Most often, both of these methods are used together to give coherence to a paragraph, although either may be used separately.

Achieving Paragraph Coherence

EXAMPLE: Stepping carefully around the straggling prickly pear I come after a few paces over bare sandstone to a plant whose defensive weaponry makes the cactus seem relatively benign. **This one** is formed of a cluster of bayonetlike leaves pointing up and outward, each stiff green blade tipped with a point as intense and penetrating as a needle. Out of the core of **this untouchable dagger's nest** rises a slender stalk, waist-high, gracefully curved, which supports a heavy cluster of bell-shaped, cream-colored, wax-coated, exquisitely perfumed flowers. **This plant**, not a cactus but a member of the lily family, is a type of yucca called Spanish bayonet.

(Edward Abbey, *Desert Solitaire*)

This paragraph is organized in an essentially spatial way. First the plant's surroundings are shown, then its leaves, stalk, and finally its most beautiful part, the flowers; this sequence follows the writer's eye as he perceives the plant. The final sentence identifies the plant for the reader. Notice the repetition of words similar to the plant's name, **bayonetlike**, **dagger's nest**, and also the frequent use of the demonstrative adjective **this**.

EXAMPLE: Many a skier drives forward, but, as his legs pass each other, he relaxes and discontinues the knee-drive. There is not as much power or extension **there**, and **such skiers** will not go so fast. **This kind of skiing** is often telegraphed by the arm movements or body position. If the body is upright, chances are the forward knee-drive is insufficient. If the arms come forward with elbows bent sharply or don't go backward beyond the hip, their shortened swing is proof that the extension is not complete.

(John Caldwell, *The New Cross-Country Ski Book*)

This paragraph's organization is based on a kind of cause-and-effect structure. A type of faulty skiing technique is introduced in the first sentence. The second sentence shows the effects of this technique on performance. The final three sentences illustrate the physical effects of such skiing which are external signs of the skier's mistakes. The last two sentences are parallel in structure, a sophisticated method of keeping the paragraph coherent. The transitional words appear in boldface.

Coherence in the Paragraph

Coherence in the Paragraph—Exercise 1

Paragraph coherence

NAME _____

Decide whether or not the following paragraphs are coherent. If they are, write _coherent_ in the space provided; if they are not, write _incoherent_.

1. Students on today's campuses have often been called apathetic; they seem to do nothing, to be interested in very little. But often the so-called apathy is simply the result of fear, whether fear of failure, disapproval, or commitment to a new set of ideas. The real problem of student apathy, then, lies in the inability of students, faculty, and administration alike to find ways in which to lessen that fear, to assure that curiosity and investigation need not be penalized. Such exploration in itself might be considered a worthy undertaking, apart from the usual categories of success and failure.

2. A football coach's job isn't as simple as it may sound. Games are won, not only on the field, but during long training sessions. Many college football players go on to become professionals. These men need many talents. The coach must find his players' strengths and use them efficiently. After training sessions, the team's weaknesses and strengths are analyzed by the coach and this is when he must make his key decisions. A good coach is a strategist, analyst, teacher, and psychologist. He must also discover the opposing team's weak points and try to make use of them in planning his own team's game.

3. More and more people these days are adopting a vegetarian diet. Many people simply feel they do not wish to contribute to the slaughter of animals. There are various types of vegetarianism. Most vegetarians exclude all meat and fish from their diet; others, however, are stricter. They exclude dairy products and eggs as well as meat. One point in favor of vegetarianism is that a vegetable diet is often less expensive than a meat-based diet. There seem to be no ill effects from a vegetarian diet if it is carefully balanced nutritionally. Some vegetarians even expand their diet to include fish and sea foods. Also, vegetarians contend that more people can be fed on a vegetable-based agriculture than on a meat-based one.

4. About five years ago I met one of the most remarkable women I've ever known. She had just been appointed librarian of the Tarsville Public Library, her name was May Gibbons, and she was seventy years old. What led her, at her age, to become librarian for such a small town was her strong conviction that people

should read and that books should be available to everyone. From her first day on the job, she was untiring. She solicited money from the City Council for library funds, collected books, instituted reading programs for children, and widely publicized the town's "new" library. This enthusiasm has been contagious, and the Tarsville Public Library is now a center of the town's life. And, of course, at the center of the library's success is May Gibbons.

5. During the first few days at a university, a student must make many difficult adjustments. The new student must adjust to cafeteria hours and cooking. Living with a roommate instead of a familiar brother or sister can mean adjusting to new demands on one's time or to new lifestyles. These problems of living with a stranger are augmented for the freshman who has always had a private room at home. Then, there are books to buy, classes to find, and a whole new schedule to adapt to. But, once the student has overcome these problems, a whole new world is opened for him or her.

Coherence in the Paragraph

Coherence in the Paragraph—Exercise 2

Achieving paragraph coherence

NAME _____

Read the following sentences carefully and arrange them in the best order to form a coherent paragraph. Explain briefly what clues led you to select your ordering of the sentences.

1. a. No matter how immature it is, it is already as rigid as a mast, with tier on tier of whorled, perfectly horizontal branches that are too short and stiff to bend.

   b. So the foliage instead of being a flat spray, as in the Eastern Balsam Fir, is a spiky bed on which the snowfall is speared and held in cottony tufts.

   c. Some, like the graceful but weaktipped Douglas Firs and the Hemlocks, bend under it, especially while young, till they look like sheeted ghosts all doubled up, or crouching, as if convulsed either with mirth or with pain, but scarcely recognizable as trees.

   d. Many other conifers have flexible needles, but those of this Fir are at once stiff and all, as it were, brushed upward to the top of the twig.

   e. If it is to escape these leafy fingers it will have to melt; the sturdy needles refuse to yield to it and spill it.

   f. Not so the Alpine Fir.

   g. Many kinds of trees that love the mountain heights must for long seasons bear great weights of snow.

   (Donald Culross Peattie, *A Natural History of Western Trees*)

2. a. An oilman who visited the ranch offered him twice his salary to come to Oklahoma and run a ranch that he had there.

   b. He called Buck Peebles, a silent wiry type who hauls cattle and household goods and Mexican shearers and goats and anything else that's willing to ride on his old truck and pay for the privilege.

   c. He was a good foreman and liked his job and liked his boss.

   d. But finally, when the offer got to three times his salary and his wife was shoving at him to think of the kids and even his current employer admitted—wryly—that he wouldn't blame him in the least for going, he agreed.

   e. They loaded on the furniture and the kids and the wife, and drove 200 miles up to the new place.

f. I knew a cedar-hill man who served as foreman on one of the new cleared ranches built by city men in that region.

g. He turned it down.

(John Graves, Goodbye to a River)

a. The more challenging game animals like deer certainly rank high.

b. Time after time we have been on field trips with seasoned mountain people who refuse to enter an abandoned house or meadow or cave because it looks so "snakey."

c. It is difficult to say what variety of mountain wildlife holds the place of honor in fireside conversations.

d. And of course there are the more dangerous ones like panthers and bears with which nearly every hunter has had his moments of terror.

e. And time after time we have been amazed at the quality and variety of tales evoked by the mere mention of snakes.

f. Few living things, however, occupy the place of respect and awe that snakes enjoy.

("Snake Lore," The Foxfire Book)

a. Once every 10,000 years or so they come close to the sun, rapidly traverse the inner portion of their orbits, and then speed back out again to the depths of space.

b. The "wind" of atoms flowing out from the sun—the extremities of the solar corona—catches comet material and blows it out into a long, luminous tail, sometimes stretching millions of miles in a direction away from the sun.

c. The solar system has many comets, which probably are huge chunks of loosely packed ices—frozen gases such as carbon dioxide (dry ice), methane, cyanogen, and ammonia, in addition to ordinary water.

d. During this fleeting visit to the solar neighborhood, the comet encounters sunlight, which melts and evaporates some of the ices.

e. Comets usually move in highly elliptical orbits, spending most of their time in the frigid regions far beyond the orbits of the giant planets—even beyond Pluto.

(Donald H. Menzel, A Field Guide to the Stars and Planets)

Coherence in the Paragraph

Coherence in the Paragraph—Exercise **3**

Achieving paragraph coherence

NAME _____

Using both methods of achieving paragraph coherence, rewrite those paragraphs from Exercise 1 that you marked *incoherent*. Underline the transitional words that you use.

Paragraphing

Adequate Development of the Paragraph
Item 52

Except for special purposes, such as emphasis, transition, or dialogue, every paragraph should be developed in more than one or two sentences. The writer must give enough information in each paragraph to explain or support adequately the topic of that paragraph. Often context will be important in determining how much development a paragraph needs; each paragraph must be seen in relationship to the paragraphs before and after it.

The topic sentence acts as the foundation for a paragraph; it will determine to a large extent how much development the paragraph needs.

EXAMPLE: Ever since man first began to travel long distances he has wittingly and unwittingly brought other creatures along with him. The dingo . . . evidently came to the island continent (Australia) as the companion of prehistoric man during the late pleistocene, so transplantation is not new. As the human population increases, and as rapid travel becomes commonplace, nonhuman hitchhikers abound: Insects and spiders accompany bananas; rats, mice and even cats sneak off ships that are loading cargo at remote, oceanic islands; and the American traveler returning from Europe brings back European cold viruses along with new watches, scarves, and ash trays (the European traveler in America does the same). Foreign organisms are spread in other ways. Agricultural animals (like pigs) and plants (like coconuts) escape readily from domestication. People also transport and release animals and plants because they like them or because they like to hunt them or fish for them. Flocks of hundreds of Australian budgerigars (parakeets) wheel over St. Petersburg, Florida, and schools of Coho (Pacific) salmon thrive in lakes Michi-

Adequate Development of the Paragraph

gan and Superior, where they give joy to fishermen and feed on anothe
recent arrival, the alewife.

(David W. Ehrenfeld, *Biological Conservatio*

The topic sentence of this paragraph (the first sentence) indicates that thre
aspects of human transmission of animal and plant life will be discussed: tha
this has taken place over a long period of time, that this has occurred withou
man's conscious aid, and that this has often been the result of conscious hu
man action. Examples are given to illustrate each of these contentions. If th
topic sentence had mentioned **four** aspects of transmission of plant and ar
mal life, the paragraph would not be adequately developed by a discussion o
only **three** aspects.

2

Once a paragraph topic has been introduced, the writer is under an obligatic
to the readers to make that idea understandable and complete. Enough info
mation should be supplied to answer the reader's main questions about th
topic. Often the basis for adequate development of a paragraph will lie in th
presentation of specific details about the general topic being discussed.

3

There are many possible methods for developing paragraphs and providir
adequate support for the topic statement. Some of the most often used at
these:

A. Supportive detail, including examples, illustrations, facts, statistics, ar
    testimony of other people
    (The paragraph in section I is developed through supportive detail. Ehrer
    feld gives examples of various animals carried long distances by man.)

B. Definition of key terms

C. Comparison or contrast of topic idea or event with an idea or event mor
    familiar to readers

D. Causes and/or effects of topic idea or event

E. Description of topic idea or event

F. Explanation of how topic idea or event operates

Any of these methods of paragraph development may be used in combinatic
as well as separately. The writer's choice among them will be based on whic
best suits the type of subject discussed in a particular paragraph, the informe
tion available to the writer, and the place of the paragraph in the whole essay

dequate Development of the Paragraph—Exercise **1**

dequate development of the paragraph

IAME _____

issume that the following sentences are topic sentences of paragraphs.
Idicate for each one what will be discussed in its paragraph. Be as spe-
ific as possible.

XAMPLE: Most of the action in *Star Wars* might have come straight from
a standard western.
To develop this paragraph, the writer will have to show what the
action of a standard western involves—good guys versus bad
guys, romance kept to a minimum, constant action, last minute
suspense, and so on. Illustrations from *Star Wars* must be
given to show that it fits this pattern.

. Spending a quiet afternoon alone can be a good way to deal with tension
and nervousness.

. Dr. Jones, the pediatrician, perfectly illustrates what a good children's
doctor should be.

. Registration can be a confusing process for the new student.

. An academic scholarship should be given only to people who meet certain definite standards.

. In many ways, Atlanta is a typical southern town.

Adequate Development of the Paragraph

Adequate Development of the Paragraph—Exercise 2

Adequate development of the paragraph

NAME _____

Read the following paragraphs carefully. Write *adequate* afte those that have been adequately developed and *inadequate* afte those that have not. Explain what methods have been used to de velop the adequate paragraphs.

1. Some people like to dance to fast music and other people like to dance only to slow music. All people dance the way they feel they can follow the beat best.

2. Many people feel that cloudy, rainy days are depressing and gloomy. But, actually, there need be no correlation between rainy days and depression. I learned this when I lived on the Pacific coast.

3. In the years that followed its founding, the town grew gradually, attracted more businesses, expanded its boundaries, and offered a greater variety of employment to its citizens. Statehood gave a great stimulus to the development of Ohio towns, and the rate of growth of Milltown quickened. In 1905, the railroad came to Milltown and with the railroad came new ethnic groups, Irish and Chinese. Milltown was on its way to becoming a large, diversely populated city.

4. The country in which I grew up was a land of great variety and beauty. As a child, I often enjoyed the warm, sunny climate and rolling hills. It was a perfect country for a child. I had a wonderful time growing up there.

5. As scouts, we learned to read the information left by the passing of people, animals, and time through the woods. Our teacher was an old man whose very survival had depended on these skills, and he impressed upon us the importance of clear sight and good memory. We learned to recognize different animal signs, to determine whether branches had been broken and rocks dislodged by animals, people, or only wind or

water. We learned which plants could be eaten and which were poisonous. We were able, after some practice, to sit quietly and watch the forest
animals go about their own business. And we learned to lay and follow
trails, often spending whole days leading one another about the woods.

The Renaissance ideal of the perfect courtier is perhaps best described
as a man whose every action and attitude would be suitable to his position. He would not flaunt his clothes or his abilities in front of others. He
would be high-born, restrained, sensitive. His reason would be taught to
discipline his whole character. Such a man may be seen in Titian's painting *Man with the Glove*, and Shakespeare could not have created Hamlet
without this dignified image of what a noble man should be.

A student coming from a small high school may often feel lonely and
frightened at first at a large university. Most of the people are strangers.
The new student feels anonymous and insignificant. He is lost in a world
not his own.

Adequate Development of the Paragraph

Adequate Development of the Paragraph—Exercise **3**

Adequate development of the paragraph

NAME _____

List the questions that still need to be answered for the inadequate developed paragraphs of Exercise 2.

EXAMPLE: Inadequate paragraph: My grandmother was a remarkable woman. She embodied the best of the pioneer spirit and left a legacy of independence for her children and grandchildren.
Questions: What is the "best of the pioneer spirit"? What specific action or actions show this spirit in the grandmother? What is the "legacy of independence"?